The Golden Age

The rural crafts practised by
John Golden,
the final proprietor of
north Norfolk's Foundry

POPPYLAND
PUBLISHING

Further details of Poppyland Publishing titles can be found at
www.poppyland.co.uk
and more news at www.facebook.com/poppylandpublishing

The Golden Age

Graham Ferguson

Opposite: John Golden in 1964, with a nineteenth
century Hutson-made Gallas plough.

Picture Credits

Archant 4, 23r, 25c, 50, 57, 60, 61l, 61r, 75l, 76c, 78l,
78c, 88, 90r
Norfolk Record Office 11, 21, 36l, 36c, 48, 64, 72l, 72c,
81c
Mervyn Mills 13
James Mindham 14/15
Peter Stibbons 16l, 16r
Norfolk County Council 17, 18l, 55b
Norfol Industrial Archaeology Society 18r, 19l, 56lt,
56lb, 56c, 59lt, 59lb, 73l, 74c, 75rt
Sky-Views 19r, 39rb, 73c
Peter Burrows 22l, 24, 25r, 26r, 28rt, 31, 32, 34, 39rt,
40l, 40c, 56r, 75ct, 75cm, 75rm, 75rb, 76lt, 76lm,
76lb, 89l, 89r, 92, 93l, 93r, 95
Iona Folliard 22ct, 39lt, 44r, 45, 82, 91c
Author 22cb, 22r, 23lt, 23lm, 23lb, 26l, 28l, 28rb, 30c,
30rt, 30rb, 38b, 39lb, 41, 54, 55t, 66l, 66r, 67l, 67c,
67r, 68l, 68r, 69, 74l, 75cb, 84r, 85r, 86l, 86ct, 86cm,
86rm, 86rb, 91lb, 94
Ian Thompson-Bell 25l, 27
Bridget Cuthbert 35, 37t, 43l, 85c, 96, 98l, 98r
Richard May 37b, 44l, 86rt
Dot Bradley 38t, 43c, 83
Lorna Fish 42, 81r
Creative Commons 51, 84l
A Dollinger 62
Janet Payne 53l
Dennis Wise 53r
June & John Richardson 59r, 90l
National Gallery 71
Major Gurney 87
Sylvia Pardon 77, 91lt

Key to Position
Left l, Centre c, Right r, Top t, Middle m, Bottom b

Acknowledgements

This book could not have been written
without the assistance so generously
given by many good Norfolk folk who, I
discovered, collectively hold a remarkable
store of photographs, documents and
anecdotes.

Full acknowledgements are recorded at
page 105.

Graham Ferguson
The Old Foundry
Northrepps
Summer 2013

Second foundry layout and activities c. 1920.
(Not to scale).

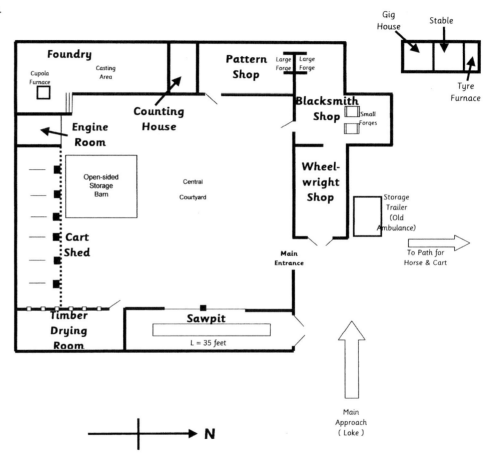

Introduction

Coffins, cars and costermongers' carts were never part of the plan. The aim had been simply to find out more about the old industrial building –now converted – in which my wife and I lived. However one thing led to another and the enterprise became wider than originally envisaged.

Living in a tranquil English village in north Norfolk, one may feel that nothing much alters from day to day. Looking back over a longer period, however, significant change becomes clear. Traditional activities familiar to our parents' generation, and even our own childhood, no longer exist. Craftsmen, with their knowledge of and dedication to specialist skills, have become superfluous, and the chain that passes on their expertise is almost broken. But our generation's achievements are based on the transfer of the accomplishments of earlier inventors and artisans and there is much to learn from their single-minded approach. While we have available eye-witness accounts and photographs, it makes sense to keep a record of the traditional craftsmanship which, as part of our heritage, should not be forgotten.

This book describes the rural crafts practised by John Golden, the final proprietor of The Old Foundry, a rectangle of buildings still standing in Northrepps, a village three miles south-east of Cromer. Although the narrative is about Golden and his men, similar methods were employed by skilled tradesmen in all parts of Britain in the late nineteenth and early twentieth centuries, up to the time when traditional workmanship collided with modern technology.

Despite its modest size, Northrepps has always produced larger-than-life figures: John Playford, born here in 1623, a noted exponent of the musical instrument called the cittern and part of a family whose members had been Lords of the Manor; Sally Bean, the nineteenth century gin-swilling look-out and smugglers' friend and – unencumbered by a husband – mother of nine children; Anna Gurney who, whilst wheelchair-bound, supervised the testing of the breeches buoy and helped support a local inventor who produced other life-saving devices; and Thomas Fowell Buxton, a leader in slave emancipation.

The most remarkable feature of Northrepps' Old Foundry was not the place but a person: the redoubtable John Golden who as carpenter, builder, foundryman, cartwright, wheelwright, sawpit operative, blacksmith, undertaker, sawmill operator, engine restorer, vintage-car collector, property owner, school governor, parish councillor, churchwarden and media personality rightfully takes his place amongst Norfolk notables.

Over the past two hundred years in Northrepps there have been, in addition to other businesses, two foundries and a timber-yard. The first foundry, unconnected with the Goldens, was established in the early nineteenth century. Shortly afterwards, on a nearby site, John's grandfather, George, set up his carpentry and woodworking operation. For about a century, this timber-yard/sawmill was, for George and later his son Frank and grandson John, the main base for their carpentry and building work. Years later, the Goldens became involved with, and subsequently acquired, the nearby second iron-foundry.

It was John Golden's facility with two key materials – wood and iron – that underpinned his wide range of skills and interests and is the basis of this account of traditional rural crafts.

8

Contents

The Golden Family Tree

This tree is restricted to the immiediate line of the ancestors of John Golden

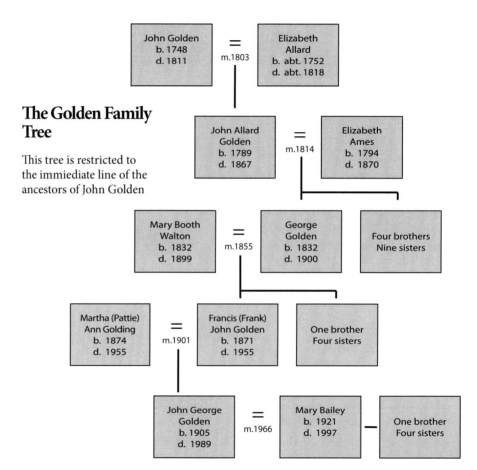

Northrepps' first foundry

The world's first industrial revolution took place in eighteenth-century Britain, and that period provided a springboard for the astonishing developments, inventions and discoveries of the nineteenth century.

Victorian engineering produced dazzling creations at home, while overseas exploration and military triumphs combined to give the UK widespread trade dominance. The development of Britain's mighty industrial centres saw millions move from rural to urban areas. At the same time, the population of the U.K. increased dramatically. In 1801, it was 10.1 million and by 1851 it had more than doubled to 27.3 million. The extra mouths had to be fed and this ensured that, despite the trend to new industries, agriculture remained the UK's biggest employer, followed closely by domestic service. Norfolk in particular, being less touched by heavy industry, retained its predominately agrarian bias in the nineteenth century. But while the ploughman still homeward plodded his weary way, new engineering techniques were having an impact on the methods and productivity of agricultural work. It was not surprising, therefore, to find that even deep in pastoral areas new industrial units were being set up, and Northrepps was no exception.

William Hutson was born in 1786 in Bodham, two miles south-west of the town of Sheringham, and grew to be an enterprising youth. In 1815, at the relatively young age of 29, and perhaps spurred by new responsibilities following his marriage to Tabitha and the recent arrival of his son William junior, he established the first foundry in Northrepps. Hutson's buildings were erected on a site which approximates to the car-park adjoining today's pub, and mention of that requires a few words about the development of the public house. We may be confident there was no pub when William Hutson set up his fledgling business, though nearby were rows of brick-and-flint cottages.

Binge drinking and debate over the pricing of alcohol are age-old issues in Britain. In the eighteenth and early nineteenth centuries the poison of choice was gin – mother's ruin – whose cheapness and ready availability led to widespread public drunkenness and general depravity as famously depicted in Hogarth's engraving 'Gin Lane'. The government took pains to try to improve matters, for example by introducing the Gin Act. Part of officialdom's efforts involved a cunning plan: they decided to encourage the drinking of beer as a wholesome substitute for gin. This new idea met with general approval. Parliament duly passed into law the Beer House Act 1830 which allowed many householders (the middle-class property owners who paid the 'poor rate' to help fund relief to the poor), on payment of a small fee to the Excise authorities, to open part of their home – often the front parlour – for the sale of beer, ale and cider, though not wine or spirits. And so it was that, in addition to the centuries-old taverns and inns, the 'beer house' came into existence.

Of the many initiatives taken by governments then and since, inciting the masses to imbibe beer surely must rank as one of the most popular. Indeed, within a year, 31,000 beer houses appeared in Britain. Our own village made its modest contribution to this tidal wave, and White's trade directory of 1836 records two beer houses in Northrepps, one alongside Hutson's foundry and the other in the Loke on the west side of Church Street, opposite what later would become the timber yard. Each must have started between 1830 and 1836.

The first licensees were, respectively, Sherman Payne and Robert Summers. Clearly one of the beer houses was sited to cater for the thirsty employees at the foundry. Because of their origin, the beer houses – nascent pubs – were set amongst a row of cottages and not on the customary main corner or road junction long favoured by the larger and longer-established taverns.

In due course – in 1851 or thereabouts – each Northrepps beer house was granted a licence to become a fully-fledged inn or public house, one choosing the somewhat grandiloquent title of the Foundry and Mark Lane Arms Inn and the other, in a nod towards George Golden's new timber yard, styling itself the Carpenters' Arms. The former establishment prospered and expanded by absorbing neighbouring buildings, whereas the Carpenters' Arms disappeared around 1858. White's directory of 1854 tells us that at the Foundry and Mark Lane Arms Inn (licensee then William Storey) farmers and dealers

assembled at 10.00 am every Tuesday for the transaction of business. Folklore has it that Mark Lane was a local seed merchant, though there is no evidence to support this. Another possibility may be adduced: Mark Lane was (and still is) the address of the London Corn Exchange where nineteenth-century brewing companies would have purchased grain.

In the early to mid nineteenth century, Northrepps had a population of about 600, considerably larger than a small neighbour called Overstrand whose headcount then was a mere 250. Half a century later, a 1906 redrawing of parish boundaries, coupled with Overstrand's subsequent building explosion, brought about a reversal in the population imbalance between the two villages. White's directory of 1836 records Northrepps as being 'a large detached village in two parts, called Church Street and Far-Street'. Whilst no map or other document of the time confirms the name Far-Street, it's reasonable to infer from White's description that this was an early term for Crossdale Street. Indeed it seems that for several decades the authorities had difficulty in determining a final name, since the 1816 Ordnance Survey's drawing had called it Northrepps Low

Street and, later, the 1881 census referred to Pond Street. That same census reveals some intriguing statistics concerning large families and their disinclination to move out of the parish. For example, Northrepps in 1881 had 31 people with the surname Woodhouse and 33 called Payne. But the prize for fecundity must go to the extended family of Risebrow (with spelling variations) of whom there were counted no fewer than 50.

Looking at the county of Norfolk, White's of 1883 lists the following trades (amongst others) : 64 iron founders; 14 brass founders; 760 blacksmiths; 325 wheelwrights; 73 thatchers; 5 bone crushers; 4 jet workers and 1 ivory turner.

With the invention of the Ordnance Survey map, 19th century Britain became the cartographic leader of the world. For our part of Norfolk, the earliest large-scale OS map is dated 1887.

Detailed tithe maps, used to provide a basis for charges levied by the church and other land-owners, had been prepared at an earlier date. For our parish, the tithe map was published about 1840, and shows the east–west run of Northrepps Street (now Church Street) with the beer

Beer house First foundry and smithy buildings

© Norfolk County Council

The 1840 tithe map extract shows the east-west run of Northrepps Street (now Church Street).

house then indistinguishable from other cottages in the row. Close by was William Hutson's foundry and smithy. The foundry and beer house developed a mutually beneficial association. Hutson was happy because riders and carriages stopping for refreshment would turn to him to have horses re-shod and carts repaired. Similarly, carters and others intent on doing business at the foundry or smithy would afterwards drop in at the beer house or pub.

Hutson's foundry became a centre for interconnected trades including those of casting, blacksmith, farrier, cartwright and wheelwright. Contemporary records name Edmund Summers as wheelwright, though some writers have described him as 'blacksmith'; he might have done both. Either way, he would have been based at Hutson's premises. Summers is widely assumed to have been involved in smuggling. There is no dispute about nineteenth-century contraband activity around Northrepps and Overstrand, and so Summers' alleged smuggling role is entirely plausible.

Using detail gleaned from early maps and other notes, we can bring back to life the village's first foundry as it may have looked in the middle of the nineteenth century. The representation on pages 14–15 illustrates how the foundry/smithy and pub in Church Street would have appeared.

In addition to its two beer houses, Northrepps in the mid-nineteenth century had a butcher, tailor, three shoemakers, four shopkeepers and 14 named farmers of whom George and James Emery's family name lives on in the address of the present-day modern homes close to the pub.

Another titbit contained in White's 1836 directory is the observation that 'on an eminence called Tolls Hill is a very fine echo, produced by a bold and lofty range of hills on the opposite side of the vale'. It would surely be instructive to test this claim anew.

The new firm of William Hutson – in due course renamed William Hutson & Son – made ploughs, pumps, drills and a wide range of other farming implements. In this rural area, whatever local farmers required Hutson would produce. For example, his business made two-horse and four-horse threshing (or thrashing) drums for use in a horse-works where, confined to a small ring, the hapless beasts walked in endless circles with their shafts attached to the thresher as the farm-worker fed in the sheaves of grain. This was felt to be progress, since at that time much of the threshing was still done manually with a flail.

When we consider that Willam Hutson was born in 1786, it may come as something of a surprise to learn that we have some – just a few – first-hand details of his life. Basic facts on birth, marriage and death have been gleaned from parish and civil registration records, but other pieces of information about his daily life have reached us as an oral record – a verbal vignette – from more than a century ago. This small miracle comes about in the following way.

In 1860, as the aging patriarch of the local foundry, Mr Hutson enjoyed travelling round the locality in his horse and cart and receiving the plaudits of those who used his farm implements. On occasions, he would allow a small boy of eleven to accompany him provided the lad helped by opening gates – some being toll gates – and by holding the horse when asked. On his trot-about, William Hutson would be recognised by ploughmen working in the fields. They would leave hold of the tails of the plough which, being a single-furrow tool, could be left for the horse to continue on its own. The men would walk down to the roadside where Mr Hutson was waiting, and courteously pass the time of day with him. Often he would give a ploughman a few coppers to buy himself some beer in the evening. The foundry owner evidently was pleased and proud simply to see the farm workers using his equipment and thus demonstrating to passers-by the efficiency of the Hutson plough. All this was absorbed

by the young lad who, some years later, began to train to do a variety of jobs including blacksmith and foundry work, as well as helping out at local properties. Like anyone, his life had ups and downs, though his most unexpected down came when he was repairing a well at Northrepps Hall. Eventually he was hauled out of the well, nursing a broken leg and a bruised ego. Despite the leg problem, he still managed to get about the village and lived to about 70. In his later years, around 1919, he often came across the teenage John Golden. The older man needed little prompting to regale John with stories of his boyhood adventures with William Hutson. Intrigued by these simple tales of village history, John stored it all in his memory. Then, in 1972, when John Golden was 67, he was persuaded to talk about his life and times. Along with much else, the Hutson yarns finally were tape-recorded and then transcribed.

In January 1859, Hutson Senior's 'increasing infirmities' obliged him to hand over full ownership of the business to his son. It appears that, as he became older, William the father became more interested in his ownership of the foundry buildings and also of other property he

had acquired, and when he died at the age of 75 in 1862, his death certificate recorded his occupation as Proprietor of Houses. The son, William Latten Hutson, by then aged 50 and already sole owner of the foundry/smithy, might have been expected to continue the family business for many more years. This was not to be, however, for just two years after William senior's death, William junior died unexpectedly at the age of 52.

It was 1864 and Northrepps' foundry suddenly was rudderless. The business had been described as an 'extensive iron works [giving] employment to a great number of hands'. Now, with the firm's prospects looking bleak, those employees and their families faced an uncertain future. But this was not the only concerned group. During the mid-nineteenth century the well-known North Walsham ironmonger Randell's had obtained plough-shares and many other metal items from Northrepps, and the foundry's possible demise threatened them with a sudden loss of key supplies.

The Randell family had to act decisively, and they did. With little delay, they arranged to take over the whole Northrepps operation, and ran that business for the following five or six years.

Life expectancy in the mid-nineteenth century was low, and there are several examples from trade directories of a proprietor's listing being switched abruptly from Mr to Mrs, presumably because a widow was continuing the family business after the death of her husband. As a case in point, during the period when Randell's owned and operated the Northrepps foundry, the Post Office trade directory of 1869 listed the 'Founder and Blacksmith' that year as Mrs Randell – clearly a determined lady. At around this time, Randell's took the key decision to establish their own foundry in North Walsham, the town they considered their home base. Their new foundry, with associated buildings, was set up around 1867 in the Bacton Road (on the site of the present-day Sainsbury's supermarket), and was known as the St Nicholas Works. In 1897 the family business of M. Randell & Sons became a limited company called F. Randell Limited.

Following the start-up of their foundry in North Walsham, Randell's transferred much of the Northrepps equipment to their new manufacturing unit. They were contracted to supply various parks, and in particular Gunton Park, and Randell's provided much of the wrought iron for the several miles of fencing.

Once their new North Walsham manufacturing unit became fully operational, Randell's were in a position to relinquish the Northrepps business which, around 1870, was sold to Edmund Curties who, as it happens, was married to one of John Golden's great aunts. His Northrepps operation, duly renamed Curties and Company, was financed by funds from the estate of John's great-grandfather, also called John Golden. Sadly, however, the Curties period came to a premature halt with the death of Edmund Curties and this, it appears, was the beginning of the end of foundry operations

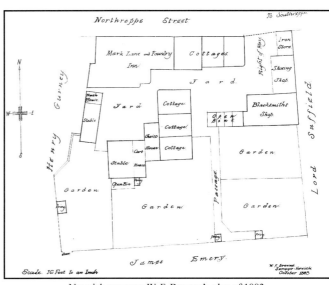
Norwich surveyor W. F. Browne's plan of 1883.

at the site alongside the pub. The year 1880 was to usher in a new era of iron-working at a fresh site a few hundred yards west along Church Street.

Before we switch our attention from the location of the pub and its neighbouring foundry, let us take a look at a detailed plan of the 1883 site layout, courtesy of a Norwich-based surveyor, Mr W. F. Browne.

It is not known what prompted the drafting

of this detailed plan, though the most plausible explanation is that it was required to support a land sale. In any event, we should pause a moment to offer up thanks to the long-departed Mr Browne for the accuracy with which he prepared his document and for the insights it provides.

At the top of the plan we see that Church Street was then called Northrepps Street. The pub is easily identified together with its then three adjoining cottages on the east side. The west cottage was absorbed into the pub as part of its building redevelopment in the mid-1980s. The other two were merged into one, and today only an eagle-eyed passer-by would spot the clues to the past existence of two separate properties. Close examination of the cottage gable-end at the entrance to the yard/car-park shows that the right-angled corner becomes curved at a lower level, as though a giant file had removed the sharpness of the corner up to a height of six feet. The cottage across the road, at the entrance to Storey's Loke, likewise has a curved corner, also about the height of a man. It is thought that the rounded shape was designed to deflect, with minimal damage, the wooden wheels of any horse-drawn carriage or cart attempting an over-

A virtual graphic, based on the tithe maps and other contemporary information, recreates Northrepps's first foundry as it was in the mid nineteenth century.

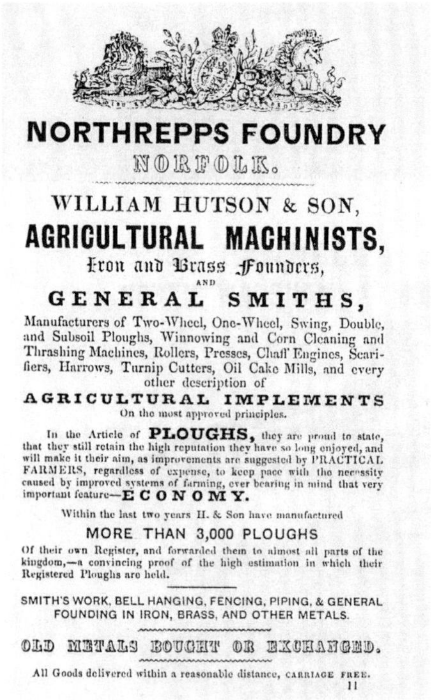

The Hutson advertisement, thought to have been published in 1850, shows the wide variety of implements produced at Northrepps. Note the willingness to make any improvements suggested by 'Practical Farmers', the emphasis on 'economy', and the proud statement of 'more than 3,000 ploughs' (in only two years). The royal warrant is prominently displayed.

ambitious fast turn into the yard or loke.

Further to the east are some of the foundry/smithy buildings. Unfortunately the sharp cut-off on the plan's eastern boundary, where Lord Suffield's name is shown as landowner, means that we don't see the additional buildings that also formed part of this metal-working complex which, by the plan's date of 1883, had been reduced to smithy work only.

Look at the other group of three cottages in the centre of the plan. Immediately to their west are respectively a Chaise House, a Cart House and a Stable – the equivalent of modern garaging in that horse-dependent era.

On the far west side are a Stable and a Wash-House, the latter a common facility in villages of the time. Its rudimentary fired-up 'copper' would have been available to any villager on payment of a half-penny so that the family's weekly wash could be done. After all, there was no mains water and wouldn't be for another half-century. Long before indoor lavatories, the plan shows three outdoor privies where, if patrons had fortunate timing, they might find some squares of newspaper still hanging on a string. As noted above, by the late nineteenth

The Randell advertisement, circa 1868, makes clear the North Walsham connection but shows the main foundry was in Northrepps. 'Norfolk Plough' may have been an alternative name for the Gallas plough.

century the first foundry alongside the pub had begun a prolonged run-down, relying just on some smithy work, while the new foundry, a few hundred yards away, build up its casting operation. Almost all the old buildings to the east and south of the pub were demolished long ago, though two original walls are still standing. Reminders of this first foundry live on in the pub name and in the nearby road called Foundry Close.

Northrepps' second foundry

We come now to Northrepps' second foundry – the one still standing today as a private home – which was started by Thomas William Burton, another enterprising man who owned an ironmonger's shop in North Walsham. In 1880, at the age of 36, he decided to expand his horizons and, mindful of the availability of experienced foundrymen in Northrepps following the closure of the first foundry, decided to use the existing quadrangle of buildings in Church Street – about three hundred yards west of the original foundry – as the base for his new foundry operation. The buildings required only slight modification to house the cupola furnace and necessary patterns and mould-boxes. Burton brought some equipment from his store in North Walsham and purchased patterns from a firm called Cubitt's (later bought out by Randell's). The new Burton foundry began making ploughs – not only Cubitt's but also the Hutson Gallas plough. Initially, both makes had wooden beams and handles or

The 1840 tithe map on the left and the 1887 Ordnance Survey map on the right enable us to bracket the date range.

tails, with the foundry production being for the metal share and wheels; later metal beams and handles were introduced. The plough-share and other metal production continued until the cessation of foundry work in 1938. At the same time, across the road in the timber yard, the wooden parts were made by John's father, Frank, and other skilled carpenters. The various components – wood and metal – were brought together for final assembly in the wheelwrights' shop. Thus the finished plough was an early example of the need to have available a number of different skills and trades.

The start-date of the 'new' Burton foundry is not listed in any records. However, we have John Golden's assertion that the sawpit (part of the foundry complex) and the sawmill (separate buildings on the other side of Church Street) had both been built in 1850. John's father, Frank, claimed that, as a nine-year-old, he witnessed the second foundry start-up in 1880. So we have John's date of 1850 and Frank's of 1880. The most likely way of reconciling these is to accept that the sawpit together with the adjoining cart-shed (for horses bringing tree-trunks) and some other neighbouring parts were erected about

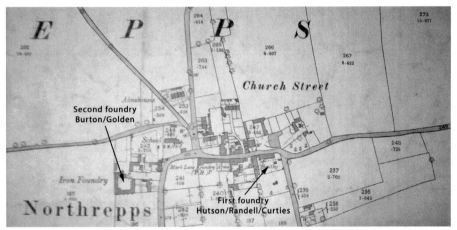

The sites of the first and second foundries on the 1887 Ordnance Survey map.

display the same area and use approximately the same scale. They're rotated to match; you will see that the 1840 tithe map shows an empty field on the exact spot where the 1887 OS map names the rectangle of buildings as 'Iron Foundry'. Certainly, then, the initial date-range for all the buildings as well as the start-up of the Burton foundry is within the period 1840–87.

We can tighten the start-date of the range by referring to the 1875 Post Office directory which lists Edmund Curties as iron founder in the old foundry. Since Burton didn't start his new operation until after Curties's death,

1850. As was the way with rural buildings in the mid-nineteenth century, other branches such as the blacksmith's forges would have been added as the need arose over the following two or three decades. Around 1880, Mr Burton came along and, we may surmise, adapted an existing section to create his iron foundry which only ever encompassed a portion of the quadrangle of buildings.

For confirmation, we can bracket the date-range using the 1840 tithe map and the 1887 Ordnance Survey map on page 17. Both

The main entrance to the courtyard of the second Foundry in the latter days of Golden ownership.

This plate simply states 'Norfolk Plough'. which, perhaps, may have been an alternative name for the Gallas plough.

A customer plate: 'John Thompson, Farmer, Hall farm, Trimingham'.

The metal plate bears the maker's name: 'T.W.Burton, Northrepps'.

The aerial shot of 1965 shows the distinctive quadrangle of foundry buildings on the left. The corrugated iron-roofed barn - shown in the middle of the foundry square - was demolished as part of the 2001 redevelopment, but otherwise the general shape of the modified property remains today. The large building at the top of the photograph is the old village hall, later demolished. Its replacement is sited on the edge of the playing field. At the bottom, slightly left of centre, is the two–storey former headmaster's house, built by George Golden.

we now have a reduced 12-year range: from 1875 to 1887. This sits comfortably with the estimated 1880 foundry start date.

Finally, we may narrow our end-date by referring to White's 1883 directory which lists newcomer Thomas Burton as Iron Founder in the new foundry. This makes the 1880 foundry start-up date entirely plausible.

There is nothing in these documented facts to conflict with John's dates. Furthermore, the 1883 plan of the pub and surrounding buildings refers only to blacksmith; the absence of 'foundry' description lends support to our conclusion that by 1880 the iron casting had already switched to the new Burton premises.

Although the first foundry (alongside the pub) had ceased iron-casting by 1880, its buildings remained intact for several years beyond that date and it's probable that some blacksmith work continued for a time. It's interesting to view the 1887 Ordnance Survey map (page 18) which identifies both old and new foundry buildings.

By 1887 the new Burton foundry was going full steam ahead whereas the old (first) foundry was almost inactive apart from minor smithy work.

An aerial photograph taken in 1965 (page 19) provides more recognisable detail. The known age of many of the buildings (except for the more recent Village Hall) provides reassurance that this picture provides a broad indication of how the site would have looked towards the end of the nineteenth century.

We've considered in detail the likely date when Thomas William Burton started his new foundry at Northrepps, but of course John claimed that his family had established the nearby timber/carpenters' yard also in 1850. Guided by the 1887 OS map, we must assume that the nineteenth-century timber-yard buildings were those shown alongside the old flint wall immediately to the west of the pub. Probably part of the adjoining open area was used as a timber-storage yard. During the early twentieth century a range of purpose-built sawmill structures was erected across a wider area and are seen on later maps.

In Burton's time it was common practice to fix metal name-plates to some of the larger products cast in the foundry. The plates displayed different things: the manufacturer, or the product name or occasionally that of the customer if he were judged sufficiently important. A few examples act as reminders of the foundry beginnings (see page 19).

Along with their North Walsham ironmongery business, the Burton family ran the new Northrepps foundry, making the Gallas plough and many other items, for more than 50 years. During the latter part of that period, Frank Golden and, later, also his son John gained experience by helping out with various foundry tasks. Around 1934 Burton agreed to sell everything to Randell's. Because Randell's then already had their own North Walsham foundry, their main interest was in acquiring the other parts of the Burton operation and thus they willingly accepted that the Northrepps foundry and associated buildings should be sold to the Goldens.

The furnace and casting operation continued under Golden ownership for some further years. With several other trades also being practised on the same site, the premises might more aptly have been called a Rural Crafts Complex. Frank and John's foundry and related work is considered in other chapters.

The Gallas plough

So far as the citizenry of Norfolk is concerned, the most celebrated item said to have been created by William Hutson in Northrepps was the Gallas plough. In later years it was to attain an iconic status

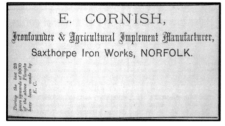

E. CORNISH,
Ironfounder & Agricultural Implement Manufacturer,
Saxthorpe Iron Works, NORFOLK.

During the last 23 years upwards of 3000 of the above Ploughs have been made by E. C.

In 1856 the Cornish company confidently advertised their business and eponymous plough. Not to be outdone by Hutson, the sideways writing mentions 3,000 Cornish ploughs; less impressively though, that was a 23 year total.

within the village, eventually receiving the accolade of being incorporated in the village sign. However, it must be said that it is hard to find many references to the Gallas. Even John Golden, ever conscious of neighbourhood history, never mentioned the G-word in his long tape-recorded interview in 1972, though he did speak of Cubitt, Hutson and Cornish, the

latter being Ezra Cornish of Saxthorpe.

Part of the problem lies with the Gallas name, for this plough has aliases. The original name was the Gallows plough, the ghoulish description derived from the resemblance to a hanging gallows of the plough carriage on which the beam rested. Apparently the Gallas was known also as the Norfolk plough, though such a generic title is uncomfortably imprecise and might easily cover other types. Sometimes, too, the term Norfolk Gallas was used. Finally, it is likely that the term 'Hutson plough' became, at least within Norfolk, an alternative name for the Gallas.

It is believed that, as far back as the 1500s, a particular plough design from the Netherlands had become popular in Norfolk, possibly because of the similarity of the terrain in East Anglia and Holland, and this machine became known as the Norfolk plough. Inevitably experience and trial and error led to design modifications and improvements, and eventually this long-gestated article manifested itself as the Gallows/Gallas. With such a long incubation it's hard to be as definite as we might wish. It seems certain that this plough evolved through development

and redesign, rather than being a sudden invention. To avoid risk to my personal welfare as I walk the local streets, however, I'll stay with the consensus view that the definitive Gallas design was perfected by William Hutson in Northrepps' foundry.

In the early twentieth century, Claude Culpin, a Cambridge University lecturer in agricultural engineering, wrote a book *Farm Machinery* (London: Crosby Lockwood, 1938 and later editions) which came to be well-regarded. In its 1938 edition, Culpin's book included these observations:

> Gallows' Ploughs possess a 2-wheeled fore-carriage which supports the beam on a saddle or collar in which it has a limited amount of freedom to turn. These ploughs are somewhat clumsy compared with the common wheeled type, and they are not as easily and accurately adjustable as the latter. In Britain they are in general use only in Norfolk, but they are the favourite type in many continental countries. The high beam gives a clearance that is useful for ploughing in rubbish, and the loose connexion between the

wheels and the beam makes them suitable for use on steeply sloping land.

We may select several ways of viewing the (Norfolk) Gallas plough. Some of the ploughs illustrated here were manufactured by Hutson or by his successor, Randell, at the first foundry; others were made by Thomas William Burton at the second foundry.

The first, reproduced, here is from the catalogue of F. Randell Ltd in the late nineteenth century. As is evident, the Gallas came in different sizes, each priced accordingly.

The small vertical blade(s) or cutting knife – in front of the main share – is known as the coulter; this helped open the way for the horizontal slice of the share.

At the 2003 'Tunstead Trosh', F. Randell Ltd of North Walsham proudly displayed a Gallas plough. The keen-eyed will see that, fixed to a post, is the same picture as one of those alongside, although taken from the catalogue of a different year.

Northrepps church has on permanent display a version (probably Burton) of the Gallas plough, or at least a main part

of it, with blue-coloured metal shaft and handles.

Gressenhall Museum (below) houses an early-nineteenth-century version of the Gallas or Gallows plough manufactured by Mr Hook of Weston Longville. A separate notice refers to a 'Norfolk Gallows Plough . . . made by William Hutson in Northrepps Foundry.'

The fifth example of the Gallas plough (opposite, top left) is an early-twentieth-century 'wooden' model made before 1910 by Thomas William Burton at Northrepps' second foundry. This item was bought at auction in 1995 by a well-known Attleborough farmer who maintains an extensive and fascinating collection of

ploughs, carts and other agricultural implements. This plough, now more than 100 years old, is the only known existing fully-complete timber-framed Northrepps Gallas with maker's plate attached.

A close-up of the Gallas's plate on the plough shown left: T.W. Burton, Northrepps

The gallows-shaped carriage on which the beam rests at the front

A sixth example is a nineteenth-century Hutson-made Gallas wooden plough (seen right in the photograph with John Golden).

Comparing and contrasting the detail in each of these photographs, it's hard to avoid the conclusion that they are not all identical. We know manufacturers copy and adapt, and it's inevitable that even the celebrated Gallas plough underwent design modifications – and imitations – over the years.

Allen Ransome, grandson of Ipswich foundry owner Robert Ransome, became senior partner in his family engineering business and, pertinent to plough names and types, observed in 1843 that 'Ploughs

of various other shapes and fashions from one imagined improvement to another multiplied to an almost endless variety'. In other words, ploughs were modified, copied and improved with such frequency that a particular design did not remain fixed for any length of time. Whatever the true situation, there's no denying the vicarious pride still felt in Northrepps village in the locally designed and produced Gallas plough.

How foundry casting is done

If, when dining out, you occasionally treat yourself to a delicious, naughty chocolate fondant, you probably consider prodding the pudding to release the heavenly, gooey melted chocolate to be far more enjoyable than contemplating the etymology of the name, and so you may not care that the word 'fondant' derives from the French *fondre* which means to melt, and that same linguistic route gives us 'foundry', a place for melting. A foundry is a factory where pig-iron is melted in a furnace, and the molten metal carried by ladle to be poured into a mould of the desired shape. When cooled, the newly-formed or 'cast' iron artefact can be lifted out of the mould-box. Like most manufacturing operations, the basic principles may be stated simply but the practical realities of production are more complex. Descriptions relate to the particular methods used at Northrepps by John Golden. Although a range of metals/alloys may be processed by a foundry, John used mainly iron, and so we restrict ourselves to that.

The furnace

The Northrepps furnace – known as a cupola –was a metal cylinder eight feet (2.4 m) high; at the lower front was a slag outlet, closed off with a hinged door in which was a 2-inch (5 cm) diameter tap-hole plugged with a tennis ball-sized lump of clay.

Sitting in the south-west corner of the Northrepps quadrangle of buildings, this oversized tin-can stood on a brick pier about 20 inches (0.5 m) above an earthen floor permanently darkened by black sand spillage. Set at a lower level than the

flooring in the rest of the buildings, the cupola working area was reached down a short flight of steps. The furnace was lined with refractories (heat-resistant bricks) and had an output rate of around 2 tons per hour.

Happily for us, in the early 1970s an accurate scale drawing was made of the cupola which, although then inactive, remained complete and in situ. The diagram on the right shows the furnace location in the south-west corner of the buildings. Also surviving are some photographs of the decommissioned cupola, still in the general area where once it was fired up – see left. These pictures allow us to identify the key parts of the furnace. At each of four corners round the cupola was a metal pillar like a scaffolding pole; these held, at roof height, a square frame which supported the furnace chimney. As with the eventual disappearance of many other items, the subsequent demolition of this chimney proved a sad loss. The 1971 extract (opposite) from an article in the *Eastern Daily Press* makes clear John's regret at acting hastily in pulling down a bit of history.

John maintained that the cupola was adapted from an old boiler from Mundesley mill. Not all those consulted agree on this, but it does seem likely.

Walter Hurn is one of the few remaining

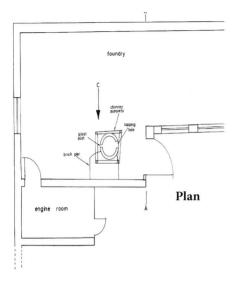

Plan

Elevation

elevation from C.

people to remember the foundry operation before it closed finally in 1938. At age 14 in 1936, Walter left school on a Friday and started work in John Golden's business on the following Monday. Today he still resides within a pony-and-trap ride of Northrepps. Reaching 90 in 2012, Walter is a charming gentleman who retains a disciplined approach and a sharp mind. His wife Janet has a bright-eyed vivacity that belies her age, and together Walter and Janet help paint a picture of a bygone period. For much of his time with the Goldens, Walter worked in the carpenters' shop at the sawmill, and he recalls how, once a week, he would leave his regular job at the sawmill and walk the 100 yards up the Loke to help at the foundry. Barring an exceptional back-log of work, the foundry operated only on Fridays.

The employees who helped (up to 1938) with casting and moulds were 'Mouldy' Payne (Head Foundryman), Bob Gray (Blacksmith), Sydney Wayte (Blacksmith), Walter Hurn (Carpenter) and, of course, John Golden. Although each had his lead task, job flexibility was essential and, when necessary, the men would help one another. The team handling the Friday foundry operation comprised Mouldy, Bob,

RARE CHIMNEY PULLED DOWN

WHAT may well have been a rare chimney has been demolished at Northrepps. But until they started to take it down, no one realised how unusual it was.

The chimney was that of a furnace at the foundry in the village which ceased work in 1938. The building is now used as a builder's store by Mr. John Golden, of Church Street.

The roof was sagging and Mr. Golden set about making it safe by removing the chimney and roofing the building over.

But once some of the old tiling and woodwork had been removed it showed that the chimney had been erected on piers when the furnace was built in 1853.

In its heyday

Sixty-five-year-old Mr. Golden said his father had remembered the "new" foundry being built, the old one having been near the Foundry Arms public-house a few hundred yards away.

The foundry had made all sorts of ironwork for the village and surrounding area, from plough shares and gratings to crab pot bottoms.

Mr. Golden has helped stoke up the furnace — which he believes began life as a boiler at Mundesley Mill. "I remember when I was still at school throwing iron on for them. The plug at the bottom came out and two or three hundredweight of iron ran out.

"I ran for the door. If that had got my legs that would have been the end of me," he said.

Another picture of the disused furnace, giving a clear view of the charging hole, two-thirds of the way up the cupola, through which iron and coke were loaded.

Walter and often John himself. The morning routine began at eight o'clock, in preparation for the eleven o'clock production run. It hardly need be said that operating a furnace and dealing with molten iron is a potentially hazardous endeavour and careful preparation is essential. Mouldy and Bob would have spent several days earlier in the week ensuring that scrap iron, pig iron and coke were available in suitable places in the courtyard. The inside of the cold cupola would have been checked and cleared of any residual slag and other unwanted material, a difficult process which sometimes required a man to clamber into the empty furnace.

Importantly, the men would have got ready all necessary moulds, of which more later. Because the furnace is a fast melter, Walter and the others on Friday morning would check that crucibles (ladles), moulds and various tools had all been placed readily to hand. Also, start-quantities of coke and iron had to be collected and stacked near to the cupola. All this took time. Once prepared, the fire-up would begin and afterwards the tap hole would be plugged with a cone-shaped ball of clay – a clay bot –applied at a safe distance from the intense heat using a bot or botting stick.

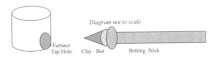

As John himself explained:
> When you started off your furnace you would . . . lay a fire like you would anything else with some shavings and wood and put the coke on, well then they would set fire to that and, 'cos we had an engine . . . start that up and the blast from the fan would blow it up. Well then after you'd got it burning you'd put so much, you'd close the front up where the slag used to come out, you'd close that up . . . Well then you'd get the furnace hot, you'd put your metal on and your pig iron on.

Gradually as the coke was fed in, a fierce heat built up.

Power for fan

Meanwhile, a few yards away in the engine room on the other side of a flint wall, the engine would be started up. This was linked by means of wheels and belts to line-shafting used to drive equipment and especially to power the fan which blasted air into the furnace through a vent hole – a tuyere – some two feet above the cupola base. When the Northrepps foundry had been established in 1880, the power source for driving the fan was an 1860 Hindley 2hp Vertical-Boilered Steam Machine; small but highly effective. Obviously the

The Hornsby-Akroyd engine at the foundry.

boiler for a steam-powered engine needs a plentiful supply of water which in the absence of mains supply was brought from a near-by well. Everything went smoothly for 16 years until, on one unpropitious day in 1896, some unfortunate soul neglected to replenish the water. After some preliminary spluttering, the boiler signalled the end of its mechanical life with a mighty explosion, blowing off part of the roof and causing consternation amongst the foundrymen. As fast as it could be arranged, the broken engine was replaced by the modern marvel of its day: the Hornsby-Akroyd 5.5 hp single-cylinder oil-fired engine. It's worth noting that, in 1890, Herbert Akroyd Stuart had filed Patent 7146, for Richard Hornsby & Sons of Grantham, Lincolnshire, for 'Improvements in Engines operated by

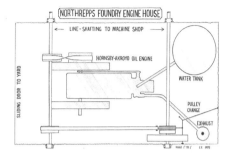

NORTHREPPS FOUNDRY ENGINE HOUSE

LINE - SHAFTING TO MACHINE SHOP

HORNSBY-AKROYD OIL ENGINE

WATER TANK

SLIDING DOOR TO YARD

PULLEY CHANGE

EXHAUST

In 1975, with the Hornsby-Akroyd engine still in position, this drawing of the engine room layout was made by Mr C Fisher. Some of the overhead equipment remains in place today.

the explosion of mixture of combustible vapour or gas and air'. Akroyd the inventor combined with Hornsby the manufacturer, and in the late 19th century their Hornsby-Akroyd pressurised fuel system, a world first, was hugely successful. Some consider that this basic design concept led to the subsequent development of the diesel engine.

An interesting feature of this new Hornsby-Akroyd creation was its hot-bulb, a separated combustion chamber mounted on the cylinder head into which fuel was sprayed. The Northrepps engine ran on paraffin, and start-up required a blow-torch to be played on the engine's hot-bulb for about 30 minutes until the paraffin inside had vaporised sufficiently and the whole mechanism sprang into life. Thereafter the heat from the exhaust gases would keep the system going. Once the engine was active, the wheels, pulleys and line-shafts would creak and splutter into action, amidst the hissing and fumes of the oil engine. By all accounts, the entire noisy, smoky, clanking, fuming paraphernalia was akin to some tortuously complicated device constructed by Wallace & Gromit.

Raw material

At the start of fire-up, the cupola was loaded with coke and then with pig iron and scrap iron, on top of which a thin layer of limestone was added. The sequence was repeated, with alternative layers of iron, limestone and coke. Any old bits of scrap iron, as well as imperfect foundry products, would simply be fed back into the cupola. As John Golden said:

Well, we used to have the pig come, 'cos that used to come by rail then, and we used to collect, cart it from the station just the same as the foundry coke. 'Cos the foundry coke . . . and coal was specially made, that isn't coke that's, we'll say, recovered like you used to from the gas works; that hadn't, that was pure and simply coke made for that job.

And about the pig iron and scrap, he said:

Well then of course that would – they would be about – the pig iron parts would be about three feet six inches long and about three inches square; but they weren't square, they were sort of D-shaped. [Also] . . . a lot of good things – what would have been thought to be good now for museum purposes – were broken up into scrap. Well, we used to buy them just for that special purpose.

Furnace production

Alternate layers of iron, scrap and coke would be fed into the furnace, in a weight ratio of 85% iron to 15% coke. A small amount of limestone was added to act as a flux to help crystallise the slag. As part of the chemical reaction within the cupola, the coke reacts with the oxygen in the blast-air to produce carbon monoxide; then a further rise in temperature from red heat to white heat – up to about 1,600° Celsius – causes causes a further themodynamic

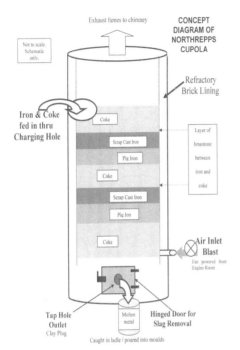

Not to scale. Schematic only.

Exhaust fumes to chimney

CONCEPT DIAGRAM OF NORTHREPPS CUPOLA

Refractory Brick Lining

Iron & Coke fed in thru Charging Hole

Coke

Scrap Cast Iron

Pig Iron

Coke

Scrap Cast Iron

Pig Iron

Coke

Layer of limestone between iron and coke

Air Inlet Blast
Fan powered from Engine Room

Tap Hole Outlet
Clay Plug

Molten metal

Hinged Door for Slag Removal

Caught in ladle / poured into moulds

reaction and molten iron begins to drip to the bottom. The cupola operation is a continuous one, and the furnace may be kept charged with raw material so long as molten metal is required.

Although not shown, the top of the Northrepps cupola had a hinged cover which could be closed depending on weather conditions.

Mould boxes

With the cupola ready to release molten iron, we must move sharply to the next stage – casting – which involves mould boxes, green sand and patterns.

A mould box has a square or rectangular shape, and may be made of wood or metal. It can be likened to a miniature room with four walls but no ceiling and no floor, though moulding work is done on a baseboard or plate which acts as a temporary floor. Depending on size and weight, the box may be used on a bench or on the floor. At the Northrepps foundry almost all boxes were metal and were used mostly on the floor. Sand is heavy, and box strength and position were critical. Usually a ridge ran round the interior of the box, helping to provide a key to grip the casting sand. The complete mould, known as a flask, consisted of a top box or 'cope' set onto a lower box or 'drag'.

Each box had a pin or guide with a mounting plate bolted on to both sides

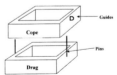

Guides

Cope

Pins

Drag

Stacked mould boxes – copes and drags – stored at Northrepps Foundry

of the metal box. The pins of the bottom box would slot into the guides of the top box, ensuring the two parts correctly and securely joined together. Larger foundries often use more sophisticated arrangements including hinges and locks for joining tops with bottoms. John didn't do fancy; he kept it simple but effective.

When setting up a mould for a plough-share – the plough's metal digging blade – John would use a 'chill'. This was a cast-iron plate on which the mould flask sits; as its name implies, the chill plate cools the molten metal faster than normal and this increases the hardness of share. In an interview, John said that 'we'd have perhaps eighteen or twenty of these chills in a row and pour along'. Then, after removing the formed shares from the moulds, the process would be repeated. In this way, John said, 'they'd run perhaps eight hours at a time and make several dozen shares.'

Sand

When a mould was to be prepared, the box (flask) would be filled with a type of sand capable of taking the shape of a pattern pressed into it. Childhood memories of sand-castles being demolished by gentle waves may make sand seem a curious choice to withstand the power of molten metal. For moulding,

a key principle is that fine-grain sand – with a low but essential moisture content – must be mixed with a certain amount of clay which helps give it a defined level of stickiness in order to hold the form imparted by the pattern, a characteristic known as the bond. Occasionally geography helps a foundryman who, fortuitously, may discover a local source of ready-blended sand and clay, known as natural bonded sand. Whether specially mixed or found naturally, the end result has to be a pliable substance with a consistency somewhat like fresh putty or children's Plasticine. When squeezed, the mould sand should take on the impression of the hand and retain that shape when released. To be acceptable, the sand has to possess appropriate properties of permeability, fineness, heat-resistance, tensile strength and so on. As you will readily deduce, sand is a scientific subject in its own right, and certain companies specialise in the supply of sand suitable for mould-making.

As ever, John looked for an easy low-cost supply source. When interviewed in 1972, John confirmed that he had obtained his sand 'from near the cliffs at Sidestrand', and that it was brought to Northrepps

foundry using a horse and cart. He simply went to his favoured part of the beach and shovelled up whatever was needed. He explained, 'you want sand that when you grip it will more or less make into a ball . . . and you'd have to have clay for lining the ladles out with. Well that [clay] used to be got from the cliff where the water ran out, you see.' In the foundry, a small quantity of coal dust is added to the sand/clay mixture as this helps prevent sand adhering to the casting when it leaves the mould and can improve the finish of the metal. In the trade, the prepared substance of sand, clay and moisture ready for moulding is known as 'green sand'. Of course, having had clay and coal dust added and having been burnt through re-use, the original red virgin substance becomes almost black and soon gives the foundry floor its familiar sooty appearance. So, in the matter of foundry sand, green contains red but looks black. (Do keep up.)

After use, the sand was kept in a pile in a corner of the foundry floor. This could be accessed for future casting campaigns, though often some new green sand had to be added to the pile if the old sand had become overly burnt by repeated processing.

Mould making

To begin, there must be a pattern – an exact wooden (occasionally metal) replica of the desired metal end-product – which will create the mould shape. The pattern, a fire grate, say, is laid on the base-plate and the four-sided box fitted around it. The box, with pattern inside, is now filled with sand. A few tiny venting holes are made in the sand with a piece of wire and then the drag box is carefully turned upside down. The moulder is presented with the underside of the pattern embedded in the flat base-surface of sand. This has to be sprinkled with parting powder which is a proprietary powder with moisture repellent properties but, as we know by now, John wasn't the man to purchase some fancy powder and so, according to the interview notes, he relied on sand mixed with coal dust: adequate and cheap. Then, alongside but not quite touching the pattern, a sprue stick (like a short broom-handle) is pushed into the sand to create what John called the feed hole into which the molten metal would later be poured.

Further detailed procedures are followed; these don't deserve mention here. Looking down on it, the drag contains a perfectly-shaped mould – the cavity from the pattern – with a small U-channel called the ingate connecting the mould to the sprue hole. This ingate channel will itself fill with metal that later will be forcibly removed.

John points out that, at this stage, the flask is on the floor and weighting provided by smaller boxes, sometimes containing additional weights, placed on top but at the corners so as not to disturb the sand.

Tapping and pouring

When the furnace melt is ready and the various flasks – cope and drag mould boxes – are set out on the floor, the operators prepare to tap the furnace by the simple expedient of using a long pointed rod, the tapping bar, to punch a hole in the clay plug or bot, to allow the molten iron to flow out into the crucible.

The crucible, or ladle as John preferred to call it, is a cylindrical metal container manoeuvred by a long carry-bar with a fixed handle at one end and a swivel handle at the other. Two men would carry the ladle to the mould where the more experienced man used the fixed handle to control the speed of pouring of the liquefied metal; the other man simply held his handle steady and allowed the carry-rod to swivel.

When the liquefied iron flows out of the cupola tap-hole into the ladle, a crust of impurities forms on top of the molten metal and this crust speedily has to be removed. As John Golden recorded,

A carry-rod holding the red-hot ladle containing molten metal from which the top-scum has to be skimmed. The far handle is fixed, whereas the near swivel-handle has yet to be slipped onto the rod and pinned in place, for carrying to the waiting mould.

At Thurton Foundry, the hot crucible is carried by two foundrymen, wearing suitable protective gear, towards the waiting mould box. In this instance the molten metal is aluminium.

'cos a boy . . . has to skim the top for there was always a crust formed on top of the, for the dirt you see the metal would separate from any impurities and then . . . a bit of thin, well, flat metal with a turned L-shape at the end . . . and you'd have to skim it to keep that back.

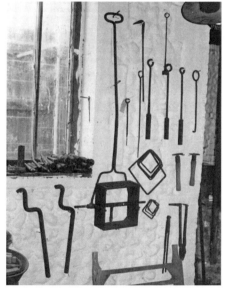

The tapping rod and botting stick are just two of numerous tools used by a foundryman, and the photograph shows a selection displayed at Northrepps.

As soon as the correct quantity had been collected in the ladle, the tap hole would immediately be closed again by the application of a bot of clay pushed in with the botting stick as described earlier. Alternate piercing and replacing of the clay bung could be repeated as often as the cupola held molten metal and there were empty moulds waiting to be filled.

Patterns

A pattern is a shaped piece of wood around which the sand is packed in the mould. When the pattern is removed, the resultant cavity in the green sand is the exact shape of the object to be cast. Making the pattern is a skilled craft and critical to the overall casting process. Get the pattern wrong and material, fuel, time and effort are all wasted.

In some cases, the Northrepps' foundry inherited patterns when they bought parts from another business. Mostly, however, both Frank and John had to create the patterns from scratch. As John explained in his interview, patterns were needed not just for farming customers but also for Cromer hoteliers who required replacements for fire grates many of which had been purchased originally from the USA. The same hotels also had other demands, as John explains:

> The hotels in Cromer and around were using coal-fired kitchen ranges and some of these had quite big cast tops and . . . we used to make the replacement tops for those and 'cos they'd be possibly an inch thick and perhaps three feet square, these big pieces with the holes in . . . [We] used to make what you call heater stoves. Well they were a square frame with a grate at the bottom . . . We used to make also grates for the open fires.

Sometimes John himself would prepare a drawing and sometimes 'a piece of paper would come in an envelope'.

In most cases patterns were made of wood, not always remaining in pristine condition. John again:

> Well initially all patterns were wood but of course eventually, you see, if they have a lot of use they would frequently have to be fixed together with nails or pins. A lot of patterns would survive but certain patterns . . . would be made from iron but of course a wood pattern is preferable

'cos the iron would get rusty and rough, and then that's a job to pull them out of the sand.

Although some of the items the Goldens produced did not need a particularly

Northrepps pattern shop showing just some of the astonishing range of patterns - from gear wheels to plough shares - kept at the foundry.

high degree of accuracy, other products demanded greater precision. As every schoolchild knows, metal expands when heated. This means that the shape taken initially by the white-hot molten metal will contract to a smaller size when cool, and this is just one of the aspects the skilled pattern-maker needs to allow for. The variation caused by expansion and contraction is made more complicated when a single casting shape contains different thicknesses.

Each item presents the pattern-maker with a unique set of circumstances. Not only must the pattern to be easy to remove from the mould, but also there must be an allowance for shrinkage and perhaps an additional allowance for subsequent machining. He must consider whether to split the item into two parts and decide whether to use wood or metal and, if wood, determine the type. Experience is essential. This job is an art.

Although the photograph shows a wide range of patterns used at Northrepps, there was always particular interest in ploughs. When asked who had designed the main ploughs, John said:

> Well I suppose they were evolved by Hutson you see, but they carried it on over the years on a similar pattern. They never well improved the plough . . . the iron ploughs were what we call Cornish but I think they were the Hutson plough. The Hutson plough were all in one piece, but on the Cornish plough the head . . . was a separate piece bolted on.

And the explanation continued in an even more complicated way. There seemed to be a suspicion about other plough-makers acquiring rivals' designs and passing them off as their own; as John commented, there was no patent protection at the time. Asked about Northrepps' plough patterns, John said that his father had created some. John apparently made others.

The largest items made by the Northrepps team were rollers used in the fields.

A view of the business

John explained that items such as plough-shares and fire grates often had their selling price set by weight. He was vague on exact figures, but said 'I think they would be only about six [old] pence a pound.' After commenting on grates being put on scales to determine weight and thus selling price, John then bemoaned the prevailing high level of wages: 'where people get ten shillings [50p] an hour now, they'd get about a shilling [5p] then . . . only them years ago.'

In response to a question about manning, he said that about seven men –never women – worked at the foundry, but were expected to be flexible in their tasks. As

John put it, 'as the work came [in] they worked in the blacksmith's shop, perhaps in the foundry, or even paint up some of the new stuff you see.' No demarcation disputes there then.

Asked about work security, John said that there was always a job for every man all year round, though the tasks changed with the seasons: ploughs in the spring, then rollers, then horse-rolls. In summer the foundry made tipplers which were used to gather in hay. They were chiefly wooden but with iron castings on the beam. Then as autumn approached, and after the crops had been harvested, ploughs were again in demand. And in winter, back to fire grates. As John said, the foundry responded to the seasons in the same way as did the farm.

According to John, there was no formal organisation, no foreman, but a simple recognition that the older men would lead the younger. John added that an older man 'couldn't read or write and yet he got everything at his finger-tips over the foundry business'. Mr Golden liked the operation to be effective but not hierarchical except that he was the boss.

The idea of apprenticeships was equally unstructured.

Well they started off as boys. They lived all their life here. 'Cos the apprenticeship as we called it . . . I don't say drift into it, but I mean they would go if the father was there, and sons would go, wouldn't they? Grew up with it, you see.

Finally, thinking back to the time when boys had started at age fourteen, John bemoaned the more recent rise in school leaving age: 'that's what we call progress' he sighed.

John was to continue working at Northrepps on building maintenance, wheelwright tasks and other activities for many more years, up until the 1980s. However specifically casting – the pure foundry operation – stopped in 1938 and a hundred and twenty years of that part of Northrepps' industrial history with its own particular skills, style and resourcefulness quietly evaporated.

George and Frank Golden

George and Mary

Let us head west, to Wales; to its capital, Cardiff. Two miles north-west of the city centre, we may find ourselves in the attractive residential area of Llandaff where, in 1832, Mary Booth Walton was born into a farming family. In a period still largely pre-industrialisation, she had a typical country upbringing and like many

The Manor House is the 1970s is little changed from centuries earlier, except for the power cables. Seen clearly at the two 'front doors' are the stone and brick porches which had been recent additions. Later, judged not to be in keeping with the original design, they were removed.

Welsh people developed a love of singing (something that, years later, her son would remember fondly).

In her teens, Mary came to Norfolk where she met and fell in love with a handsome young carpenter called George Golden. Even for a period when large families were the norm, George must have considered himself somewhat unusual, for he was one of 14 children of John and Elizabeth Golden. On 27th May 1855, English George married Welsh Mary. The newly-weds moved into the Golden family home, the Manor House – now more prosaically 21 Church Street – a large thatched dwelling dating from Tudor times and standing in the centre of Northrepps village. This imposing residence is said to have been built around 1482 by the Playford family, one of whose seventeenth-century descendants, John Playford, became a noted exponent of the lute-like cittern and is commemorated on the Northrepps village sign.

The Manor House, with its Tudor origins and later additions, possibly started as two semi-detached houses. Generations of Goldens had lived in the Manor House since about 1730. On account of its large size, the Manor House was divided in two by George and Mary who lived in one half.

George was a competent and enterprising carpenter, for it was he – as an 18-year-old –who established the timber business that in later generations was to flourish as the village sawmill in the area now occupied by Emery's Close.

Over many years, local communities had appointed their own parish constables. In 1829 the Metropolitan Police Act was introduced. Then in 1839 came the County Police Act and the Norfolk Rural Police Force; these helped create a more formal national and regional structure. Even after this legislation, however, a number of small villages continued to value the influence of a local uniformed man and so, shortly after his marriage in 1855, George Golden was appointed to the honorary position of Northrepps Parish Constable. It has been reported that the parish constable was under no obligation to turn out until he was paid a shilling. In those days, hardly a Saturday night passed without George having to attend at the local pub. He was a strong man, however, and usually his mere presence would nip trouble in the bud. More than a century earlier, in April 1731, one of George's forefathers, John Golden, had been appointed to that same position of parish constable.

Frank and Pattie

As the years went by, Mary and George had six children, Francis being the last-born in 1871. In line with the custom of bestowing nicknames, the young Francis John Golden came to be known universally as 'Frank' Golden. Mary would often sing while working in the house and Frank delighted in hearing his mother's melodious Welsh voice.

In 1880, when just nine years old, Frank had watched Burton create the new foundry in one part of the quadrangle of buildings. As he entered his teens, we may be confident that Frank proved to be a conscientious youth who took his chosen trade seriously, for in later life, and within living memory of some present-day Northrepps residents, Frank was widely regarded as a first-class exponent of carpentry. When not carrying out maintenance of local buildings, he worked on various tasks in the timber yard.

Now let's switch our attention to Hindringham, a charming village a few miles south-east of Sheringham, where we focus on the family of one particular local farmer, William Flood.

On 31st October 1865, in Hindringham parish church on Church Hill, William's daughter, Elizabeth Daplyn Flood, married John Golding, a farmer from Hainford. (The family names of Flood, Daplyn and Golding are still to be found in Hindringham.)

In time, Elizabeth and John Golding had

The photograph of Pattie (Martha Ann) is thought to have been taken around 1900, shortly before she married Frank; she would have been about 27 years old.

two daughters, Minnie Mary and Martha Ann, and a son, William Flood. In the fashion of the time, Martha Ann was given a pet name, Pattie, (though some villagers later used the style Patsy). She was an agreeable young lady and, in her mid twenties, her path crossed with that of the youthful Frank Golden and after a few years' courtship they decided to get married. Doubtless the similarity of the Golding and Golden names would have been fuel for the village wits. On 23rd April 1901, when she was 28 and Frank 30, Golding and Golden were married in the parish church at Hindringham, the bride's home village. They then set up home in Northrepps. Four years later, on 24th May 1905, Pattie and Frank greeted the arrival of a baby boy, John George Golden.

As the years went by, Pattie was much involved in village activities. She is remembered as being small in stature but big in heart. The wife of one Golden employee recalls how Pattie provided her with a weekly supply of butter and milk, something not only generous but also remarkable during war-time rationing. At other times,

Pattie would appear with jugs of fresh water, a gesture appreciated in that period before mains supply arrived in the mid-1950s.

Although some kept to the respectful title of Mrs Golden, many of the village children knew her as Aunt Pattie and she took a great interest in everybody and everything. Whilst Frank was quiet and work-centred, Aunt Pattie was always willing to receive or pass on scraps of village news. At church she took round the collection plate, and some suspected that she noted how much each had donated.

Pattie and Frank had a pony and trap, and Pattie kept a field of lucerne or alfalfa as

Frank's 1918 cash book shows that half-a-crown (two shillings and sixpence or 12.5p) got you into Cromer. Then you paid the same fare to get back to Northrepps.

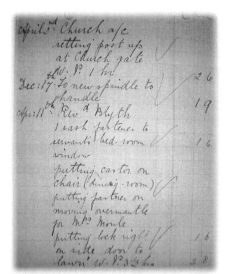

The 1918 job record shows, amongst other things, the cost of a sash fastener fitted to Rev. Blyth's servant's window, a reminder of those times when it was usual for a rector to employ live-in servants.

feed for the animal. The pony-and-trap operated as a kind of taxi service, as we know from Frank's cash book of 1918. Relative to average wages at the time, the trip was pricey and presumably used by the villagers only on special occasions.

At Christmas, Pattie would always do something for the employees, typically

distributing parcels of socks or some other useful item. Her warm-hearted character was combined with resourcefulness; and her son, through nature and nurture, began to display a similar shrewdness.

Building and maintenance

On his 1901 marriage certificate, Frank described himself as 'builder', and in the early years of the new century his activities were focussed on house-building and property maintenance, often involving timber-work such as making windows and doors. Frank regularly was asked to carry out maintenance jobs for Northrepps Primary School, whose governors' meeting minutes on 5th July 1905 stated: 'Some small repairs were ordered to be done by Mr F. Golden and the Chairman agreed to see Mr Golden respecting the same.'

And some years later, on 13th October 1910, the minutes included: 'The Clerk was instructed to obtain an estimate [from] Mr Golden for work re offices and to forward same to the Education Office.'

Just as the school looked to Frank when maintenance was needed, so too did the Rector, Rev. Alan Blyth. A glance at a page from the Golden Jobs Record of 1918 provides examples of the work done both at the Church and at the Rectory; costs are shown in pounds, shillings and pence.

The letter

Despite the cold wind of mid-October 1910, Pattie left the door ajar and stared at the letter; she recognised the handwriting on the envelope and her intuition told her it contained news she couldn't face. Later that day, Frank was able to comfort her. 'What if the worst happens?' she kept repeating. 'Should we go ahead? Can we do it?' She needed his reassurance and support. 'Hold you hard, girl', Frank said in a gentle but firm tone. 'Let's talk it over.' Later that night, overcome with emotional and physical exhaustion, but secure in the knowledge of Frank's full support, Pattie drifted off into a fitful sleep. They were in agreement. She knew what had to be done, and a journey lay ahead.

Building work

During the early part of the twentieth century, building work remained a significant part of the Golden business, and Frank's invoice, although describing the business as Agricultural Engineers, reveals in the sub-headings just how many areas (excepting undertaker) were associated with building and maintenance.

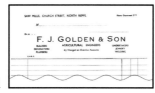

Although the passage of more than a century makes it difficult now to identify all such Golden building work, some examples do still exist. On Church Street, a few yards east of the (second) foundry, is the former schoolmaster's house, built around 1860 by George Golden, father of Frank Golden. More recently, the building was for four decades the home of well-known villagers Vera and John Woolven. Some of Frank's own work may also be seen in Sidestrand.

The photograph, taken around 2005, shows four houses (1–4 Seaview Cottages), built by Frank and John in Sidestrand in 1925 as council houses. The building site had come from a local farmer, Mr Starling, who was paid £4 compensation for the loss of his land.

As regards the tenancies of these council-provided homes, the minutes of a meeting of Sidestrand Parish Council on 8th September 1925 included the following statement:

> Recommendations for occupiers of four Council Houses at a rent of between 4/- and 5/6 [20p & 27p] per week:
> Mr J Henden (3 children)
> Mr J Bullimore (2 children)
> Mr C Dix (3 children)
> Mr C A Chadwick

Although it's not absolutely certain, we may presume that each gentleman had a wife. When it came to the serious business of agreeing tenancy arrangements, however, it appears that formal dealings were exclusively with the men.

Moving in during December 1925, the tenants doubtless were thrilled with their new accommodation which boasted a scullery containing bread oven, coal-fired copper for washing clothes, two cold-water taps and a range. Another cold-water tap fed a storage tank. However, you might consider these delights to have been offset by certain deficiencies: namely, no bathroom, no kitchen, no drainage and no electricity. Household cooking was done on a second range in the main living room. Outside there was an earth-closet. Needless to say, the houses today have been updated to modern standards.

Part-way up Nut Lane (Quiet Lane) in Northrepps, shortly before the sharp left turn, the dwelling now named Woodland House was built by Frank and John Golden in 1936 for the Harrisons, then a well-known farming family who had two children, a boy and a girl. John Golden became god-father to the daughter, Dorothy. The house has been upgraded and extended since it was first built.

The blacksmiths

In addition to his main areas of expertise, Frank spent time helping in the Burton-owned foundry across the road from his sawmill, and in this way gained experience of casting and metalwork.

Frank's work on making wheels for carts required close cooperation with the

blacksmiths Sydney Wayte, Bob Gray and Jimmy Cooper. A photograph taken in the 1920s shows Frank with his splendid moustache, blacksmith Bob Gray in the centre and an unidentified third man (possibly Sydney Wayte or Jimmy Cooper). The trio are in front of one of the smaller buildings later demolished. A curious many-spiked device sitting on the ground

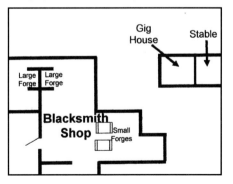

is a toppler (sometimes 'tippler'). Pulled by a horse, the toppler acted like a giant rake as it collected the mown hay. At intervals, the farm worker would tipple or topple over the rake, dumping the accumulated hay as a 'rickle' and then continuing afresh with hay-gathering. Other men would use their pitchforks to put together five rickles into a hay-cock. Topplers frequently needed their metal prongs repaired or replaced, hence the involvement of Frank and the blacksmiths.

The blacksmiths' shop was located at the north-west corner of the old foundry. One section remains, an integral part of the existing building, containing two large back-to-back brick forges now doing duty as fireplaces. A smithy extension containing two smaller forges (used mainly for smaller jobs such as horseshoes) was long ago demolished, although clues to its existence can be seen in site photographs.

It's instructive to review the photographs which show one of the large remaining forges as it once was and as it now is. A key component for a blacksmith is the bellows and the photograph illustrates how these were sited and operated. The horizontal metal handle was set on a wooden trestle

The forge, before and after gentrification for the modern home

the pumped air to play directly on to the flames.

The same forge, gentrified for the converted home, retains some sense of its former power but displays certain key differences. If you can be bothered to count the bricks, it will become clear that compared to the modern arrangement, the level of the fire-base formerly was higher, and that of the floor somewhat lower; the combined effect permitted the blacksmith to stand with the fire-level conveniently at working height.

Although not in either photograph, the forge would have had a metal canopy, and the brickwork above the fireplace still has its fixture marks.

The word 'blacksmith' is thought to derive from the black appearance of the oxides on the surface of the raw iron, and from the need to smite – later 'smith' – the metal. And plenty of smiting was done by the traditional blacksmith who at one time had to beat slag into low-carbon iron to create wrought iron. In more recent times, mild steel became the smithy's preferred choice of raw material.

The need to beat hot metal brings us to two of the smith's essential tools: the sledgehammer and the anvil, and the picture

fulcrum so that the longer end, giving extra leverage, was close to hand as the smith stood at the forge. The shorter end was attached to the bellows and pushed them up and down as the smith worked the handle. The funnel from the bellows passed through the brick wall and allowed

As one looks straight up the approach driveway, part of the old smithy extension, with one chimney evident, can be seen immediately behind the ambulance storage shelter.

(overleaf) shows an anvil in Northrepps smithy. The anvil has a curved end or horn, and a square end or heel. This distinctive shape has evolved over centuries to enable

Careful scrutiny reveals two chimneys, since demolished, which show at one time where the two smaller forges had been located.

A number of smithy jobs were undertaken, but in the early twentieth century the two most common jobs were shoes for horses and tyres for wheelwrights. Frequently these tasks were carried out using the smaller forges, one of which is pictured above

An anvil at Northrepps smithy.

the greatest variety of jobs to be done with the maximum efficiency.

When dealing with metal, the smith must heat it to a suitable temperature and, conveniently, heated iron provides its own colour guide. At first, hot iron becomes red, then it alters to orange, and finally is yellow. If subjected to even more heat, the iron eventually changes to white at which stage it melts.

Personal details

Frank was noted as a modest, courteous and kindly man, and a skilled craftsman particularly in carpentry. He was well-known in the village and, as mentioned earlier, had been appointed to the honorary position of Parish Constable which entitled him to carry a pair of handcuffs. According to a later account by John Golden, Frank lent them to the police one night to help with an arrest, but the handcuffs were never returned. As John remarked, 'I believe he was a bit annoyed about that'.

Frank and Pattie enjoyed the proverbial long and happy marriage. In 1951 they had celebrated their golden wedding and on that occasion Frank presented the local church with a special table he had made from 325-year-old oak beams which at one time had been part of the belfry.

Some of those who worked with John in 1955 still recall him coming in to the carpenters' shop in early January that year and, speaking in a quiet voice that mixed emotion with practicality, said, 'I'm afraid my father died last night. Now would you get on with making the coffin.' Frank had died on 3rd January 1955, at the age of 83, and a few days later was buried in Northrepps churchyard.

Is it possible for someone to die of a broken heart*, a condition that appears in no medical textbook? We can't be sure, but the fact is that, just twelve weeks after burying his father, John had to deliver another sad message. On 25th March, Pattie had died, aged 81.

Frank's will, which had been drawn up many years earlier in 1922, left his builder's plant and tools to John, and the majority of his estate to Pattie. The gross value of Frank's estate was £8,152. By present-day standards this sounds a modest figure, but we should remember that in the mid-1950s such a sum would have purchased three or four family homes. In any case, there's a lot of detail not available: how family property was owned, whether trusts had been established, what gifts, if any, had been made and whether bank accounts or investments were held jointly with others.

Pattie's will, drawn up at the same time as Frank's, originally had left all income to Frank and, on his demise, most of the capital to her son, John. After Frank's death, Pattie added a codicil providing for certain legacies but otherwise leaving the Estate (gross valuation £8,961) to her son, John.

Frank and Pattie's lives spanned an era of unprecedented change. When they were born Charles Darwin was alive, the petrol engine had not been invented, nor had radio, penicillin, powered flight, the electric light bulb or the telephone.

As a woman, Pattie had not been allowed to vote until a change in the law in 1918 by which time she was 44 years old. The period they lived through included Custer's last stand at the Battle of Little Big Horn, the Gladstone and Disraeli premierships, two Boer wars with the relief of Mafeking, the death of Alfred Lord Tennyson and the establishment of the Commonwealth of Australia.

Through it all, they remained true to their Norfolk roots, living a quiet rural existence, with Frank taking pride in his craftsmanship and Pattie engaged in the ebb and flow of village life. They worked conscientiously and were always mindful of others – as good an epitaph as one might wish for.

The passage of time and the effect of lichens combine to present a challenge in reading the inscription. So far as can be discerned, it states:
GOLDEN
Francis John
3rd January 1955
and Martha Ann
25th March 1955

* On 14th November 2010 the Sunday Times carried a report 'Broken Hearts are a real killer' on a study undertaken by Professor Paul Boyle and his research team, which concluded that people are most likely to give up on life within six months of losing their partner.

John Golden

Childhood

John George Golden was born to Pattie and Frank Golden in Northrepps in 1905. Frank belonged to the Victorian era, which ended with the Queen's death in 1901, whereas John was born an Edwardian. John's birth date happened to be the same as Queen Victoria's – 24th May – which accounts for it being known in times past as Empire Day.

At age four, in 1909, John started at the village school, which had been established in 1879. He progressed well and proved to be a bright lad, but with a predilection for the practical over the academic. As he was to recall many decades later, John's main childhood hobbies were making or repairing anything mechanical he could get his hands on. From an early age, his habit of carrying nuts and bolts in his pockets earned him the sobriquet John Bolt, a nickname that stayed with him into adulthood.

At school, in common with all new pupils, John had to write on a slate. This may sound like something from the Flintstones, but the old imagery lives on, for today when we plan a fresh start, we still wipe the slate clean. As they became older, children were taught to write in the spindly 'Phillip's semi-upright'. Pupils learned their tables by chanting them in unison, and discipline was strict: a rap on the knuckles was not unusual and for more serious misdemeanours a caning on the hand was the standard punishment. Unexplained non-attendance prompted a visit from the school attendance officer; invariably this had the required effect.

As for secondary schooling, the Education Act 1902 handed education over to Local Education Authorities [LEAs] and introduced grammar schools which offered scholarship places. One such grammar school, with a long and distinguished

Class L of Northrepps Primary School in May 1911. There is no full listing of names available. Amongst present-d villagers who knew the mature John Golden, the majority assesses six-year-old John to be the long-legged youngste the front row, second from the right. Standing on the far left is head teacher George Walwyn, who lived in part of t thatched dwelling just north of the Goldens' Manor House and whose son Jack also attended Northrepps school. T years after this photo was taken, Mr Walwyn died at the young age of thirty-nine and was succeeded as Head Teac by Mr Freeman.

Two young Edwardians: the tall John Golden, then aged about seven, with his cousin, Philip Copeman, who was one year younger. The photo was taken about 1912.

history, was Paston School in North Walsham, founded in 1606 and where Lord Nelson and his brother William had once been pupils. In 1908 a new scheme made Paston School a public secondary school under the auspices of the local authority. John enrolled at Paston School in 1916.

Each day John would walk along Bull's Row, passing one of the village wells above which was a pump with its lion's mouth, and then go over Toll's Hill to reach Overstrand railway station where today the station building and passenger underpass remain evident despite conversion to a private home. The train that John caught was on a line opened to passenger trains in 1906 (it closed in 1953) and operated by the Norfolk & Suffolk Joint Railways Committee (in turn owned by the M&GN and the GER). This N& SJRC branch line started at Cromer Beach Station (opened 1887) and briefly

The monthly return ticket was issued by the Norfolk & Suffolk Joint Railway Committee. Seemingly the price had been raised to one shilling and ten pence (9p). A schoolboy such as John would only ever have travelled third class.

headed towards East Runton and then looped round eastwards, going through Norfolk's only railway tunnel (we can hardly say its 'longest') to take it under the main Cromer–Norwich line, and so to Cromer Links Halt (opened in 1923) where it would disgorge happy golfers before steaming on to Overstrand. Thereafter the track headed south-east, following the landward side of the main coastal road and passing through Sidestrand Halt (opened in 1936), Trimingham (1906), and Mundesley-on-sea (1898), after which the line swung inland to Paston & Knapton station and then to North Walsham Town station (1881).

In the summer months the train was much used by holidaymakers travelling to and from the fashionable resorts of Overstrand and Cromer. Listening to the chatter of visitors, John decided that he much preferred the mechanical hiss and smell of the steam train as it took him and his school-friends to North Walsham each morning and back to Overstrand in the afternoon.

Each day when he got home, schoolboy John found his greatest pleasure in helping his father with carpentry jobs, often working by the light of an oil lamp. In an interview in later life, John remembered as a twelve-year-old being involved in making wagons, tumbrils and other horse-drawn farm carts.

John also confirmed that, at the tender age of 12, he was permitted to drive an old car.

44

Overstrand station in 1930, as John would have found it some thirteen years earlier, as he clambered onto the steam train bound for North Walsham

Much as today anyone is free to jump on a bicycle and pedal along the highway, so in the early twentieth century anyone who might appear to be 17 and was capable of sight and movement, and doubtless also some not so qualified, could get into a car and simply go. The driving test was introduced in 1935.

It would be misleading, however, to pretend that a peaceful bucolic environment for a happy boy in Northrepps was typical of the broader world in 1917, because the Great War was raging in Europe. Victory then seemed a long way off. In Norfolk, as elsewhere in the UK, there were soldiers home on leave and, as we know from the war memorial in the local churchyard, Northrepps parish lost 23 young men – a distressingly high number for such a small community – including names such as Payne, Reynolds, Risebrow and Silver as well as three of the Golden extended family. In a tightly-knit village like Northrepps, John would have known the families who had suffered loss. John himself was too young and his father too old to have been called up; in any case, those operating a small business supplying farmers with essential agricultural implements would have been deemed to be in a 'reserved occupation' and thus exempt from service.

His teens

As he entered his teenage years, John grew taller, and a family photograph shows a gangly youth towering over his contemporaries. This picture, taken in the garden of the Manor House around 1919, shows Frank and Pattie Golden seated. Standing at the back, the tall figure is 14-year-old John Golden, just before he left school, and alongside him are two of his cousins, Ada (Dolly) and Philip Copeman.

Standing (back centre) : Maud Freeman (daughter of Northrepps School Headmaster): Seated (L to R) : Philip Copeman [19] (JG's cousin); Ena Burdett [15]); Nolan Golden (cousin of JG and later noted bell-ringer); Dorothy Smith; John Golden [20]; Jack Summers: Sitting (front) : Cecil Silver

Dolly was five years older than John, and Philip one year younger.

In common with many of his pals, John had always intended to leave school as soon as legally permitted. Ironically, however, just before his hoped-for release, the Education Act 1918 raised the compulsory leaving age to 14 and so John had to wait until summer 1919 to gain his freedom. Straightaway he started to train as a carpenter in his father's business. We know from his own subsequent recollections that he happily tackled many tasks and, because he had been helping part-time for several years, soon became proficient in a number of crafts in which later he would excel.

In 1925, Whit Monday fell on 1st June, and as it was a sunny day a group of Northrepps youngsters decided to go off on a mass bicycle ride along the coast road towards Sheringham. As was the custom, the young gentlemen wore suit and tie. There were few cars in those days and the eight cyclists would have had a delightful time pedalling along, laughing and joking and enjoying the sea view. One of them had had the presence of mind to take a camera, and when the gang stopped for a break during the outing, a passer-by was persuaded to record the group for posterity.

The teenagers knew each other well. Many years later, Ena Burdett produced a private publication titled *More Rains* – an anagram of her married name Ena Morris – about her life in Northrepps and elsewhere. She wrote that she became a life-long friend of Maud Freeman, the headmaster's only daughter, and, as teenage girls will do, formed a shrewd assessment of the boys. For example, she said 'Philip was more fun than John who was interested only in cars.' Referring to John's mother, Ena commented that 'her great joy in life was her son, John, who was an extremely obedient boy'.

John's mother

John's mother, Pattie (or Patsy), played a key role in the administration of the Golden father-and-son business. For example, it was she who calculated wages for the employees who, each Saturday, dutifully lined up outside the Manor House and then waited to be called in singly, with hat removed, to receive their cash. A former employee recalled that occasionally she would say something like, 'So, have you been a good boy, then? Well, here's an extra sixpence for you.' Such financial largesse, it has to be said, was a rare if welcome occurrence. Bill Pardon remembered having had to complete a time-sheet showing hours against job numbers, indicating that Pattie maintained some kind of job-costing record.

Pattie was involved in many aspects of village life and quite naturally also took a strong interest in her son's development and well-being. Awareness of his mother's belief in him gave John an inner confidence which helped him make a success of his business and also apparently encouraged him to seek a measure of celebrity status. And if we were to explore further, we might find that the same strong maternal influence explained in part why John had few girlfriends and delayed marriage until almost retirement age. But here we risk straying off-course.

His maturity

What sort of man was John Golden? Physically, he was tall. Estimated by some to have stood at six feet four inches (1.93 metres), John would have been an imposing figure in the pre-war period and, if so disposed, somewhat intimidating to his smaller-stature work-mates. His schoolboy moniker John Bolt continued to be used amongst colleagues. His cloth cap rarely left his head and it's proved almost impossible to find a photograph of him without his traditional headpiece in place. It's said that the accumulation of grime on the back rim of his cap would have allowed the growing of potatoes – Golden Wonder, of course. He commonly addressed others as 'old friend' and, when asked how business was doing, invariably gave the reply, 'Struggling, just struggling', a phrase some felt ironic particularly in retrospect once the value of his estate had been revealed. We know John remained under the influence of a strong-willed mother. He had the successful businessman's essential attribute, persistence, and was conscientious in working at his tasks in the foundry and sawmill. And almost everyone recalls that, in his various dealings, John was careful – very careful – when it came to money. For example, on one occasion he asked an employee to use a Golden vehicle to drive to another town to collect some items for the business. On the return journey, the car broke down, and only after a lengthy repair could the vehicle be driven back to base, pushing the worker into the overtime period. A few days later the luckless employee found his pay contained zero overtime due to 'unproductive hours'. It is easy to regard such stories – and there are many – as evidence of a miserly character, but this would be to misrepresent the man. In business, there must be rules, and John stuck to these, over-rigidly perhaps, but nonetheless correctly. He viewed things in a literal way, though his precision invariably was accurate even if lacking the leniency others might have wished for. His alleged parsimony was balanced by occasional impulsive acts of generosity. The daughter of one villager remembers with affection, now more than 30 years later, how John presented her, for no particular reason, with a sovereign threaded on a neck-chain, a simple but elegant piece of jewellery he had made in his workshop. Socially, John was a lifelong teetotaller, as he readily pointed out to others.

When talking to others, John had a somewhat disconcerting mannerism: he would close his eyes. For those unfamiliar with this mild eccentricity, only the continuous voluble monologue issuing from the mouth of the apparently somnolent yet upright figure reassured the bemused listener that his interlocutor in fact remained in something more than suspended animation.

John started at a young age to buy old

Austin cars and this remained a life-long passion. Another impressive assemblage was old stand-alone petrol and steam engines, of which more than 30 were stored in the blacksmiths' shop. According to an eyewitness, the majority were runners even though not fully restored. Amongst them were a charging engine from Homersfield, the last such engine to have been used in a rural telephone exchange in Norfolk, and a Stuart engine with associated charging parts. One of the most interesting items, subsequently hauled out from under a bramble patch, was a Norwich-made Richards & Watts steam engine. When eventually sold at auction, the Richards & Watts was bought by a keen collector who lovingly restored it; the buyer's full and excited account is posted on the internet. John's obsession with collecting and hoarding was far-reaching. Over his lifetime he acquired an astonishing range of items. Some were relevant to his work, like the First World War Frost carpentry planes kept in pristine condition in their original boxes; others satisfied his mechanical interest, such as the engines mentioned above; and some seemed to defy logic, like the penny-in-slot barrel organ, the child's wicker commode chair and his collection of top hats, bowler hats and frock coats, though the latter might have been inherited from the family's early days as undertakers. John would collect just about anything, and those who worked with him became familiar with his pony-and-trap, and later a car-truck hybrid, arriving at the yard with - depending on your viewpoint - treasure or junk which would be deposited wherever the vehicle happened to grind to a halt. It is said that John alone knew where everything was stored; fortunately for him there was no need to demonstrate to his workers the virtue of striving to be employee of the month in a good-housekeeping competition.

John earned the respect of his men in a number of small but telling ways. For example when, as will happen from time to time in any business, boss and subordinate had an argument (an up-and-downer as John called it) the contentious matter would be forgotten the next day. John held no grudges.

One interesting business sideline was the production of kindling. The kindling apparatus was a massive machine ten feet (3 m) high, located between the tyre furnace and the reading room/clubhouse. Pre-cut pieces of wood, 9 inches by 10 (23 by 25 cm), were fed via a conveyor into the electric-motor-driven machine where an eccentric on the flywheel raised and lowered angled cutting blades, creating triangular-shaped kindling pieces.

John enjoyed frequenting agricultural fairs, and was a notable attendee at the Royal Norfolk Show, rolling up in one of his vintage Austins. Also, as a well-known member of Norfolk Steam Engine Club, he would bring along for public display some of his precious collection of engines which inevitably excited the curiosity of other aficionados. In this way he achieved a measure of local fame, at least amongst those who shared his obsessions. But soon his prestige spread more widely as radio and TV stations started taking an interest, and progressively he metamorphosed into a fully-fledged media personality. He would help burnish his growing renown by despatching letters to the local newspapers, usually pedantically to clarify some fact or statistic. In his later life no radio or TV production about North Norfolk was complete without the obligatory interview with Northrepps' own local character. There can be no doubt that John relished his celebrity status.

We should remind ourselves that in John's younger days – in the 1920s and 30s – the village had no electricity, no mains water and no main sewage system. In some respects it owed more to the medieval period than to the twentieth century. Light was provided by oil-lamp, water was pumped from a well and spurted through a 'lion's mouth', and privies or soil-closets were located at strategic points to be shared by a group of neighbours.

A cheque

There are not many business records surviving from John's time, and one of the few documents retained on file is a used cheque, number 12S/04541. Its date is

1934 when John Golden was 29 years old. The cheque is drawn on Barclays Bank, but in smaller print we see Gurney's Bank,

which was founded in Tooley Street (now Pitt Street) in Norwich around 1770 by John (John of Brooke) Gurney and his 'taller' brother Henry Gurney. They traded successfully and eventually joined with some other banks to form what is now Barclays Bank. It seems that to provide reassurance to former Gurney's Bank customers, the new enlarged Barclays decided to print both the Barclay and Gurney names on cheques for a number of years, in much the same way as, in recent times, Aviva continued to show the Norwich Union name alongside its own.

On the right-hand side of the cheque is a two pence stamp-duty imprint, a reminder of the cheque-usage duty that was repealed only in 1971. When we bemoan the current range of stealth taxes, at least we can find one that is no more.

Next, we can see one of the few examples of John Golden's signature; this is in his capacity as Treasurer of the Church Street Reading Room which today, converted to a private home, still

stands just a few short paces from the Golden Foundry. In 1858 John Henry (Jackey) Gurney built the reading room and established the Post Office which, at that time, had Mrs Susan Storey as postmistress. Another reading room was set up in Crossdale Street with the help of public subscription. At a time of few libraries or other public facilities, the reading rooms provided a welcome gathering place for the local men to read newspapers and to play cribbage, draughts, billiards and dominoes; there was a strict no-alcohol rule. A generation later, John Henry's son (who had the same forenames but was known as Jack) built the almshouses in the village and also rebuilt several barns and cottages. According to Verily Anderson in *The Northrepps Grandchildren,* the reading rooms were as much for local folk to be read to, as to read for themselves. She adds that Jack Gurney's brother Richard and his wife Eva would go to the reading room where they would read aloud to the inhabitants. Today the reading rooms and almshouses lack any plaque or other sign to remind us of their former purpose or of the past generosity of Jackey and Jack. (One source indicates that, alongside the Church Street reading room, the long narrow section of the building – now partly garage and partly house – was an early ten-pin skittles alley, though it has not been possible to validate this.)

The payee on the cheque is Mr Freeman, almost certainly the same strict-but-fair Northrepps primary school head teacher who lived in the schoolmaster's house between the foundry and Church Street and whose daughter Maud had been part of teenage John's village group.

We can only guess at the reason for paying him five shillings [25p] – possibly for donating books or other documents, or perhaps for giving extra tuition to those adults who needed help with reading.

Never underestimate a grubby old cheque. It may have tales to tell.

Romance

Pauline was excited at the prospect of being escorted to the pictures. Few of her friends had ever been taken out by a boy who owned a car, and she felt a mixture of apprehension and exhilaration as she waited for John to arrive. Her dreamy thoughts were disturbed by the piercing honk of a car horn and, looking round the curtain, she saw the Austin 10 waiting on the street outside, with John at the wheel.

The trip to the Regal picture house in Cromer was delightful, and Pauline imagined she was a princess gliding along as they passed pedestrians. She became aware that she had hardly stopped talking since getting into the car, and paused for a moment to allow John to speak, but he seemed to be concentrating on the road ahead and said little until the car was parked. In the Regal's foyer, which was brightly lit, John bought her a ticket and then, to her surprise, went to the refreshments bar and returned with an ice cream which, graciously, he presented to her. This, she could sense, was the start of a special evening.

His words came as a jarring blow: 'Well, got to go now.'

'What? What? John, what are you saying?' Pauline could feel a sinking sensation in the pit of her stomach.

'I have to go back. But I've given you a ticket and an ice cream.'

Pauline stared disbelievingly, unable to find any words, while a thousand bluebirds crashed to the ground.

'Yes,' John continued in his monotone, 'got to get back now. You see, I have to build a coffin.'

This oft-related tale of John's unromantic outing may be apocryphal, but the point is that, to all who knew him, it sounded believable. He had followed his mother's instructions literally, taking the young lady to the cinema, and buying her a ticket and an ice cream. Then, having fulfilled his specific duties, he felt free to head back to the important business, seemingly uncomprehending of the wider social context. The tale may be a joke told at John's expense but, as they say, many a truth spoken in jest.

It is claimed, or maybe just suspected, that over the years John had been out with a few girlfriends including, exotically, a German lady. If so, such dalliances remained discreet.

Family status

John apparently had an inner conviction about how things should be, coupled with a desire to declare publicly matters he judged important. Such certainties could reveal themselves in unusual ways, often linked to the importance of his family's history and sometimes with a sting in the tail.

For example, in January 1960, for no reason that is evident, he sprang into print with a letter to the *Eastern Daily Press* to tell the world about his grandfather's role in the local church, and at the same time to have a side-swipe at those who had carried out some poor quality refurbishment.

On another occasion John's view of the prestige of his family name led him to overstep the mark when he attempted to rename the road junction area where the village sign is now located.

Over the centuries, six generations of Goldens lived in the Manor House. It is said that, back in 1800, the area immediately outside the Manor House had been known as Golden Square. The name had continued into the twentieth century, although its usage diminished until John decided to resurrect it. Certainly Golden Square has a fine ring to it, and the name exists elsewhere: in London's Soho, in Warrington and even nearby in Cromer, just off West Street. However, it is unlikely that John had any of these worthy examples in mind when he decided that his family name again should be accorded the status befitting, as he saw it, one of the notable dynasties in the parish. A Golden

Square sign was fixed to the wall outside the Manor House, and on official papers – his will being a case in point –his address was recorded rather grandly as The Manor

Nordrups Church

Sir—The parish clerk at Northrepps Church was my grandfather, George Golden, who, by his deliberate timing on leading the responses no doubt added to the numbers attending the church. I have read that children used to see if they could repeat them twice time the congregation said them over once.

It was through the Rev. W. R. Jolly's insistence that the clerk should lead the responses that my grandfather was asked to fill the post, which, although he was a churchman, rather cramped his style. Mr. Jolly, I have heard, was a great preacher, and drew a congregation from far and wide, and when my grandfather took the offertory (he used a box he made himself) he only held it to the visitors, not the parishioners, enough being given to maintain the church expenses.

During Mr. Jolly's stay in Northrepps the church had a thorough internal restoration, some of it being near vandalism. The floor slabs were moved and some buried, the screen removed (reinstated in 1911). Mr. Jolly was Rector from 1869-74, then going as a tutor to the Royal Family.

My grandfather was clerk at Northrepps for 30 years—1870-1900—when he died, aged 69 years.—Yours faithfully,

JOHN G. GOLDEN.

Northrepps.

House, Golden Square, Northrepps.

John's attempt to re-introduce an eponymous village centre met with less than wholehearted enthusiasm from many Northrepps residents. In any event there is no record of the local Council, who have the final say on road names, ever heeding John's efforts to impose a street appellation, and the name never caught on in the modern era, except in one convoluted way. Because the nearby foundry buildings formed a square shape, sometimes people visiting or investigating the old foundry understandably but incorrectly assumed those industrial buildings to be Golden Square. Naturally this only added to the general confusion and no doubt helped persuade John that street naming was a venture too far.

John's standing in the village was recognised in several ways: he was, at various times, churchwarden, parish councillor and school governor.

John's marriage

As far as his friends and colleagues were concerned, middle-aged John had settled into the role of the eternal bachelor and so it was a considerable surprise to everyone

– possibly including himself – when, in 1966 and just a few weeks before his 61st birthday, he announced his intention to marry.

Mary Bailey, born on 5th May 1921 and thus 16 years John's junior, was the eldest daughter of Mr & Mrs George Parkinson-Bailey of The Grange, Wood Norton. It seems that the two had met through John's business dealings with Mary's brother. There are no tales of how long the couple had been courting, to use a term that feels apposite for John, and so their romantic trysts possibly were confined to the Reepham locality.

On Wednesday 30th March 1966, in the parish church at Wood Norton, midway between Fakenham and Reepham, John and Mary took their vows. The best man was Ken Watson, husband of one of Mary's four sisters, and the officiating clergy were Rev. F. J. Smith (Wood Norton) and Rev. D. L. Ainsworth (Northrepps). The 44-year-old bride wore a French blue silk two-piece with matching beehive net hat and carried an orchid buttonhole. It seems that the preparations beforehand had been kept low-key, and on the morning of the wedding John asked his employees

if they would like to attend. All said they would, and accordingly were allowed to leave work early in order to have sufficient time to dress suitably for the service. After the ceremony, bride, groom and best man travelled in John's 1927 vintage Austin 12/4 to the reception for about 50 in the Crown Hotel in Fakenham. The wedding ceremony and the reception were pleasant affairs; the bride looked radiant, John was a handsome bridegroom and the guests helped create a cheerful ambience. Only a miserable spoilsport would mar this harmonious picture by mentioning the reduction of a half-day's 'non-productive hours' in each employee's wages at the end of that week. Oops.

With their natural courtesy, Northrepps folk welcomed Mary into the village. Perhaps understandably, however, it was less easy to gauge whether she felt entirely comfortable in her new surroundings. Like any couple, John and Mary each had to make small adjustments to accommodate the other, and some felt they could discern the changes in John. It must be said,

however, that John and Mary enjoyed a happy marriage that was to last 23 years until John's death in 1989.

The village sign

Like every self-respecting community, Northrepps has its own village sign incorporating a coat-of-arms. As you might guess, John Golden was involved in its erection. Created in 1977 to commemorate the Silver Jubilee of the Queen's reign, the sign still stands proudly in the centre of Northrepps at the confluence of five roads

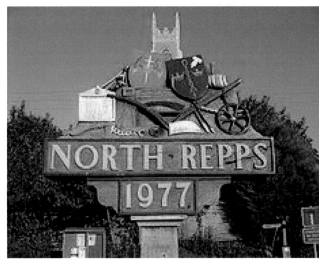

and close to the old Manor House.

The sign was designed and painted by David Ainsworth, the then rector, the carving having been done by Derek Gardner. One of John's carpenters, Bill Pardon, did the joinery work, and the building of the whole structure was undertaken by John Golden himself. The sign, which is a splendid example of the genre, contains no fewer than eleven separate items. For the benefit of the uninitiated and as a reminder for locals, the official explanation is reproduced below.

1) The parish church of St Mary the Virgin is represented by its tower.
2) The left shield bears one of the symbols [of Mary], a reference to the words of St Simeon, 'A sword shall pierce through your own heart also.'
3) The right hand shield bears that of St Benet's Abbey, because William Rugg (or Repps) was its last Abbot before the dissolution.
4) The breeches buoy was first tested here, under the direction of Anna Gurney.
5) The barrel and post relate to a smuggling incident concerning a chief preventive officer named Hickman.

6) The Thornhill railway bridge represents the fact that there are 17 such bridges in the parish.
7) The poppy reminds you that you are in Poppyland. A description of the area was penned by the journalist and writer Clement Scott.
8) The Gallas plough, widely used until 1920, was made at the foundry here.
9) The radiator is that of the Rolls Royce Silver Ghost. Henry Rolls developed this engine whilst staying here.
10) The open fetters refer to Sir Thomas Fowell Buxton, a great advocate for the abolition of slavery.
11) The cittern, a lute-like instrument, refers to John Playford, born here in 1623, who wrote a book of lessons for this instrument.

Any Radio 4 aficionado whose memory stretches back a few decades will surely recall John Timpson, one of the 'Today' programme's notable presenters. Norfolk was Mr Timpson's adopted county and he produced several books about the place including two specifically covering around 170 village signs throughout the county. And his conclusion at the end of his labour

of love? Why, the winner of his newly-created MIPEI award for the village with the Most Information-Packed Explanatory Inscription goes to Northrepps. When John Timpson's books were first published in 2002, the Northrepps Explanatory Notes had been displayed in a wooden casing fixed to the sign's supporting post, but after the casing suffered damage the notes were relegated to a corner of the more protected main notice board.

School centenary

Having been founded in 1879, Northrepps Primary School was ready to celebrate its centenary on 14th July 1979 at which time the head teacher was Roy Trot. Some years earlier John had been a school governor but by the anniversary date had handed his duties on to another.

According to an 1979 article in an unidentified local newspaper, John and Mary had commissioned special Centenary Plates. These displayed pictures of the school as it then was and also as it had been 100 years earlier. The 33 pupils were each to receive one of the commemorative plates, a generous gesture by John and Mary.

John Golden's death and succession

John died in 1989 after a short illness. On 16th March 1990, roughly ten months after his death, John's will was published; his estate was valued at £1,003,893 gross (£1,002,731 net) all of which was left to Mary. Of course the local newspapers made much of the fact that his estate had reached the nice round number of one million The property – see the map on the right –which John owned and which passed to Mary, comprised the Manor House (including land and buildings considerably beyond the house itself), the sawmill site (reaching further southwards than the main timber-yard), the foundry

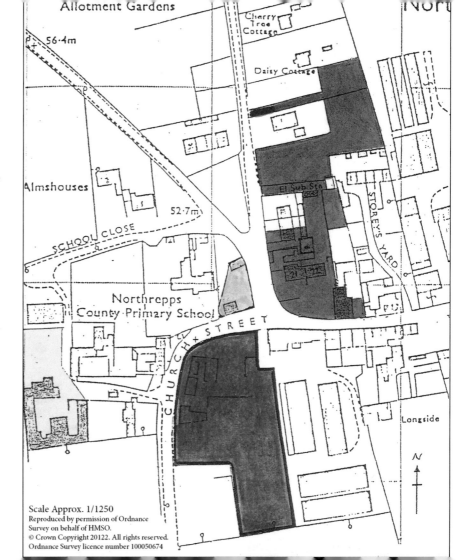

Century plates

Northrepps, I hear, is one of the next schools to celebrate its centenary. This is on July 14th when the primary school plans a celebratory open day.

What makes this centenary slightly different is that Mr. and Mrs. John Golden, of Northrepps, have had special centenary plates made. One design shows the school as it is and the other the school as it was.

The school's 33 pupils will be presented with their plates on July 14th. In the meantime, Mr. Golden — a former pupil and ex-governor of the school — and the headmaster, Mr. Roy Trott, are searching for other former pupils.

The school's records, incidentally, stretch back to 1890, but the earlier books have been lost.

Scale Approx. 1/1250
Reproduced by permission of Ordnance Survey on behalf of HMSO.
© Crown Copyright 20122. All rights reserved.
Ordnance Survey licence number 100050674

site (stretching further north than the present-day demise) and the house now known as School Barn. At one time John also had owned three cottages in Bull's Row, but these had been sold earlier during his lifetime.

After John died, his widow decided to move out of the Manor House which she considered unnecessarily large, not to say excessively costly, for one person. She arranged for a modern residence to be built nearby and this, named Golden House, stands in Church Street to the right of the entrance to Emery's Close. Mary moved

as many as possible of her former antique items into the new house, where she is reputed to have lived mostly on the ground floor.

Mary Golden, née Bailey, died on 2nd November 1997, aged 76. Her body was committed to the same grave in which John had been buried. The gravestone commemorating both lives is close to the north-east corner of Northrepps church.

Unlike John, Mary had never enjoyed or indeed expected celebrity status, and so her death and the subsequent publication of her will prompted little comment in the local newspapers. Mary had been one of six children and, after dealing with estate duty, the bulk of her estate of £563,080 was shared equally amongst her four sisters and one brother. However, before that residual share-out, she left a number of legacies. Certain specific sums went to her siblings; additionally she left £2,000 for the John Golden Memorial Fund with the

income being paid to Northrepps Church. Also there was £2,000 to the local doctors' surgery, £2,000 to Cromer Hospital, and £1,000 to Wood Norton Church where she and John had been married in March 1966.

The timber yard and sawmill

Frank and the wood yard

For many years the Goldens' business base had been the timber yard (later the sawmill) – sometimes known as the pyghtle* – the site today occupied mainly by the modern residences of Emery's Close. In Frank's time this wood yard included a number of operations and stores such as carpenters' shop, paint shop, ironmongery

Smartened up for garden use, John's former office. Under the flower basket, is a two-hinged flap which was the letter-box.

store and office. Progressively Frank introduced new tools and equipment, all machinery being powered by line-shafting from a Telemite oil-fired engine. Electricity arrived in the village in the 1930s and most of the equipment was then electrically driven.

Today, if one stands in Church Street and surveys the range of smart new homes in Emery's Close, it seems impossible to believe that any part of the old sawmill structures might still exist. Surprisingly, one of the original buildings remains intact, not far from its original place but now hidden from public gaze.

In the 1990s Mary, having arranged her possessions indoors, turned her attention to the outdoors and made a minor but interesting decision: she resolved to keep John's sawmill 'office'. Looking like an overgrown shed, it was placed in the front garden of the newly built Golden House, where it stood for several years. After Mary's death, a subsequent owner sensibly decided to relegate the office to the rear of the property where today it does service as a garden shed, just a few paces from the site of its previous incarnation.

This is as good a moment as any to skip back across the road to the Foundry quadrangle of buildings, amongst which was – and remains – the long sawpit running along the eastern length. It was built in 1850, of brick, six feet (1.83 m) deep and 35 feet (10.7 m) long with weather-proof cover. This was before power sources such as oil or electricity became available, and manual labour was used to slice large tree trunks into manageable planks that were then carted the hundred yards across the road into the timber yard to provide suitable material for the carpenters.

* Pyghtle - a small enclosure of land

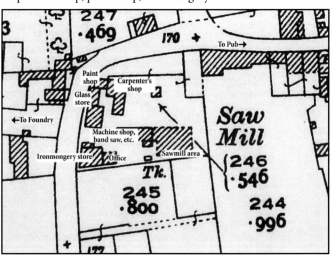

The photograph, although from a more recent era, illustrates the open plan structure and the lean-tos.

Log-handling tools used to manoeuvre heavy logs into place ready for cutting.

A 'timber jill' used to shift heavy planks and tree trunks. The timber was carrier at axle height, keeping the centre of gravity low.

This interdependency between sawpit and timber yard would have continued until the wood yard installed its own powered sawing facilities and thus became known as the sawmill. The sawpit may have been used intermittently since then for specialist jobs; it is said that John used it on at least one occasion to help shape a long mast for a sailing ship.

In the 1970s, the Northrepps sawpit was thought possibly to have been unique of its type in Norfolk. Today that claim surely must be unassailable.

The wood yard or sawmill used open-plan and lean-to structures for ease of movement of tree trunks and pieces of timber. The open style of the yard and its buildings made it a happy hunting ground for village children. As Ena Morris recalled from the 1920s:

The woodyard was very exciting – great oak logs everywhere, waiting

Nicola Bateman (top) and Julia Burrows (bottom) demonstrate the cross-handled saw and depth of the pit. The beam shown was merely support for the tree trunk which would have been laid lengthwise along the full stretch of the sawpit. Working their way along the truck's length, skilled operators displayed great precision in slicing the log into several flat planks of remarkable evenness. The hapless worker at the bottom of the six foot (1.8 m) deep pit , and on whom all dust and dirt fell, is thought by some to have given rise to the expression, 'underdog'. The upper man, of course, was top dog.

to be sawn up for coffins, door or planks, and the sawdust and shavings making a lovely smell. Mr [Frank] Golden, a large, lovely man, would always say, 'Hello, my maid!'

Calamity

On the evening of 29th June 1928, Frank and his son, John, walked back to the Manor House. They felt a mutual satisfaction with a productive day's work. Village life was unhurried, their firm was expanding, and they had every reason to be content with both business and personal matters. Certainly they could have had no premonition of what the following 24 hours would bring.

At about 6 am the following day – Saturday 30th – an early-rising villager first noticed the smell and then heard the crackling noise. He raised the alarm with the one word no sawmill owner ever wants to hear: 'Fire!'

The Goldens' timber yard was ablaze.

As any fire-fighter will explain, the three

In the centre column, an article from the Cromer and North Norfolk Post of Friday 6th July 1928 detailing the problems experienced by the Cromer fire brigade.

TIMBER FIRE AT NORTHREPPS.

SHOP COMPLETELY GUTTED.

Cromer Fire Brigade's Difficulties.

A fire broke out early on Saturday morning in a timber yard owned by Mr. F. Golden at Northrepps, and but for a change in the wind and the strenuous efforts of the villagers there might have been a disastrous conflagration, as it was the fire was confined to a carpenter's shop, in which door and window frames had been stored, and this was gutted.

Owing to the inadequate means of haulage the Cromer Fire Brigade was unable to assist, and was actually stopped when halfway to the scene of the fire, an hour after the call had been received. The fiasco was by no means the fault of the members of the Brigade. The call was received at 6.20 a.m., and within five minutes the firemen had assembled at the Fire Station and had the engine out and were waiting for a lorry to haul it to Northrepps. Captain T. L. Randall and 2nd Lieut. E. W. Harrison drove to Northrepps in a motor car, arriving at 6.35 a.m., and decided upon the position of the engine in relation to the water supply. Time went on and the lorry did not arrive, and the villagers indulged in sarcastic remarks at the expense of the Brigade.

In the meantime the members of the Brigade were fuming at the absence of a lorry, and this had to be manhandled on to the road from a field near the L.N.E.R. Station before it could be used.

Damage to the extent of £200 to £300 was done before the fire could be got under control by helpers from the village, and but for the change in the direction of the wind adjoining properties might have been involved.

requirements for a conflagration are combustible material, a supply of oxygen and an ignition source. The sawmill, filled with stacks of wooden posts, planks and sawdust, together with its airy buildings fanned by a summer breeze, readily satisfied the first two essentials. The trigger for ignition was less obvious but evidently real.

In modern times we are thankful for the courage and effectiveness of our fire-fighters, and we take for granted the reliability of their equipment. But in those days, whilst human bravery and efficiency were just as admirable, their machines were less so. A contemporary news report tells a sorry tale of mechanical failure. The local fire engine was a static device often known as a 'Steamer' because its steam pump was used to force water through the hoses. The steamer needed a lorry to haul it, and 1920s lorries were notoriously untrustworthy. With commendable speed, Cromer Fire Brigade's Captain Randall and 2nd Lieut. Harrison arrived by car at 6.35 and took charge of the situation. But without their engine/steamer, the two officers could only stand by helplessly, symbols of impotent authority outlined in the glare of the flames.

The crowd of onlookers grew, and the ridicule began: 'Hey, Fred, get some of grandma Summers' old stockings – at least then they'll have some hose.' We can imagine the rest.

Using buckets and other water-containers, the locals managed to dowse the flames, and by the time the lorry and steamer arrived, the job was done and the vehicle headed back to the fire station.

The accident could have been worse. A fortuitous change in wind direction helped restrict the damage which affected only the carpenters' shop. Other wood-yard buildings escaped lightly and, more importantly, the fire did not spread to nearby homes. Neither then nor subsequently did the Goldens insure against fire loss, a fact that might tempt us to tut-tut at their lack of prudence; but this would be unfair. The premium for cover of the wood yard with its rudimentary buildings, flammable materials and absence of any extinguisher system would have been prohibitive. Every business has to weigh risk against expense, and the decision not to pay premiums – effectively to self-insure – may have been a sensible (not to say lucky) business choice for, with

hindsight, we know that the sawmill did not suffer another fire for the next 60 years. On each occasion, the cause of the fire was never determined.

Extinguishing the flames didn't eliminate the controversy, and the case of the fire engine without traction became a cause célèbre in the village. Sympathy came from the church and protest from the Parish Council. The August 1928 edition of the parish magazine carried the following item:

> Universal sympathy with Mr & Mrs F. J. Golden was felt in the Parish and neighbourhood at the disastrous fire which occurred on the premises in the early hours of Saturday June 30th. We are most thankful that adjoining premises were not involved, though for a time there was great danger. Mr Golden is most grateful for the splendid way in which all worked to extinguish the flames. The Parish Council have sent a strong letter of protest to the Cromer Fire Brigade authorities at their unreadiness to cope with such an outbreak and their inability to render the services which they had stipulated to perform.

For the Cromer Fire Service, this had been an embarrassing incident, but their misadventure did not stop there. On the return journey, two firemen travelling in the lorry complained of hot feet. Only when the crew's attention was caught by the frantic gesturing of two lady pedestrians was the reason discovered: the fire-lorry itself was on fire. This time, the flames were extinguished promptly. Not surprisingly, the Northrepps saga prompted intense debate within the local Brigade. A hastily-convened special meeting resolved 'To recommend that the Council purchase a Motor Fire Engine with the least possible delay'. Shortly afterwards, a 'self-propelling motor fire engine' was acquired.

John and the sawmill

For several generations of Goldens, from 1850, the timber yard or sawmill remained central to the family's business operations. (Frank Golden purchased the freehold from some members of the Gurney family only on 16th December 1935; presumably the Goldens had rented the site before that date.) The size and extent of the sawmill's heavy equipment – for handling, storing, cutting, sawing, lathing and planing, together with the machinery to generate and transmit

Above, investment in heavy equipment and below, open-sided storage huts.

power – is evidence of the large financial investment built up over many decades. Much of the equipment dated from the early 1900s and was still in use more than three-quarters of a century later.

The yard contained a range of sub-sections including the machine shop (which housed band saws and suchlike), sawmill area, carpenters' shop, paint shop, glass store and ironmongery store.

Inevitably most of the activities in the foundry affected the sawmill. For example, casting patterns were mostly wooden and were fashioned in the carpenters' shop. Wheelwright and cartwright work needed some blacksmith input but also called for skilled woodwork. Any task undertaken at the long sawpit would have been associated with sawmill work. Most building and maintenance jobs would have had a mixture of timber and metal. And of course some assignments such as coffin-making were dealt with exclusively at the sawmill. Thus the sawmill/ timber yard remained a key focus for almost every job, even those ostensibly foundry-only tasks.

And that made the events of Armistice Day 1988 especially devastating. Sixty years, four months and eleven days after the previous similar disaster, fire struck again at the timber yard in the wee small hours. Like gunfire, the cracking of the blazing roof material roused nearby villagers at one o'clock in the morning. In the Manor House, Mary woke first and soon she and John, then 83, had a

A MAN of 83 told yesterday how he watched with his wife as sparks from a blazing sawmill threatened to engulf their thatched home.

John Golden, of Church Street, Northrepps, near Cromer, could only watch as fire destroyed the sawmill he owns and which has stood in the village for 148 years.

As he stood among the ruins of his once-thriving business, Mr Golden described the blaze as "a total disaster".

Firemen were sifting the debris yesterday to discover what started an inferno that swept through the timber-framed buildings in the early hours and threatened nearby homes and a turkey farm.

Villagers had raised the alarm at 1 am when they were awoken by what they thought was gunfire.

Fire destroys sawmill, but house escapes

They discovered flames ripping through the John Golden Yard sawmill, and showers of sparks sweeping towards their homes and the adjacent turkey sheds.

Mr Golden said his wife Mary woke him and they watched from a bedroom window, thinking their thatched home was also about to go up in flames.

"Sparks were blowing right over our house. If they had lodged there the house would have gone, too. It's a good job a gale was not blowing."

Mr Golden said the corrugated-roof sawmill and much of its equipment dated back to the early 1900s.

"It's a total disaster. I do not know if I can rebuild. None of the mill was insured — the premium is what I call prohibitive," he said.

The sawmill was established by Mr Golden's family in 1840 but it was not known how much of its ancient equipment could be saved.

Yards from the fire is one of four turkey breeding units owned by Cherryridge Turkeys. Stockman Gordon

Risebrow said there was panic all around as the sawmill "went up like a tinder box".

"We were worried. There are 3000 birds in the shed. The heat was tremendous and the shed became smoke-logged but the birds are okay," he said.

Station Officer Richard Moore, of North Walsham, took charge of two Cromer fire appliances which fought for an hour to bring the flames under control and damping-down operations ccontinued until late in the morning.

section containing both timber and various large powered saws and other heavy equipment representing many years of significant financial investment.

terrifyingly clear view from their upstairs bedroom window. Their horror at the wood-yard destruction was aggravated by fear over the risk from sparks to their ancient thatched home.

Fire crews from Cromer and North Walsham worked efficiently to bring matters under control, but the damage was done. The blaze affected mainly the large central

It was this section – the heart of the business – that was destroyed. Some other buildings, including the carpenters' shop, remained relatively unscathed.

Like his father before him, John had not insured the buildings, equipment and materials, for the premium would have been prohibitive. As to culpability, some villagers suspected youthful mischief getting out of

hand, though others voiced doubt about the rudimentary electric cabling which had dangled like strands of spaghetti within and between buildings. Fire investigators never were able to determine the cause of the blaze.

The commercial damage was obvious. What we don't know is just how deeply such a catastrophe – the destruction of a significant part of the family business built up over generations – might have affected John emotionally. We can only report that six months later, his health failing, John was taken to the West Norwich Hospital where he died on 6th May 1989, just 18 days short of his eighty-fourth birthday.

One might reasonably suppose, given the extensive destruction caused by the November 1988 fire and the subsequent death of John Golden in May 1989, that little else newsworthy could possibly happen. Unfortunately, not so.

On 20th May – just 14 days after John's death – villagers were alerted by cracking sounds and, once again, had reason to rouse Mary, for the sawmill was ablaze. This time the fire affected mainly the carpenters' shop which had escaped the worst of the blaze six months earlier. Mary was stunned; here was another fire in the same general area, at the same time of night and within months of the previous incident. In her mind it was all too much of a coincidence and she made her opinion known to the reporter who turned up the following day. The press article in the Eastern Daily Press on 22nd May 1989 gave prominence to her view that it had been a deliberate act of vandalism.

Privately some may have shared Mary's judgement but, as with the previous blaze,

no specific cause was ever identified by the formal investigation which followed.

And if for a moment we jump ahead to more recent times, to Saturday 18th April 2009, villagers were obliged to stand helplessly watching part of the disused poultry-processing plant just yards from the site of the former Golden sawmill going up in smoke, and many must have wondered about history repeating itself.

Blaze was arson says widow

A GRIEVING widow believes an arsonist is to blame for two massive blazes which have destroyed many of her husband's treasures. Detectives spent the weekend probing a blaze which wiped out a woodyard at Northrepps, near Cromer, which belonged to well-known resident John Golden who died only two weeks ago.

The fire, which started early on Saturday morning, came only six months after a blaze destroyed his nearby sawmill which had been used by his family for nearly 150 years.

His widow, Mary Golden, said yesterday: "Both the fires started at about 1am, and it's just too much of a coincidence. There's no way it could have been accidental — it must be deliberate.

"Poor old John has only been in his grave for a week, and I can't think who would want to do this. Somebody must have a grudge against us; it's horrible."

Mrs Golden, whose husband died a few days before his 84th birthday, said: "I'm so worried about where they will strike next. I am scared stiff about going to bed at night."

Firemen from Cromer, Sheringham and Mundesley spent more than three hours tackling the blaze at Mr Golden's woodyard at Church Street, Northrepps, before dawn on Saturday.

The fire destroyed two post-war Austin 16 cars, among Mr Golden's cherished collection of old vehicles, and many pieces of vintage woodworking machinery and equipment which he treasured. Mrs Golden said the site was not insured.

Jane Robson, whose bungalow overlooks the yard, said: "It was just a wall of flame, with sparks flying everywhere, and when the asbestos roof started cracking it sounded like fireworks.

"Dense smoke was swirling everywhere and even the tar on the road was alight."

Last November's blaze at Mr Golden's sawmill destroyed thousands of pounds worth of equipment and sent showers of sparks sweeping towards his thatched home in the centre of the village. A fire brigade spokesman said later that the damage was so extensive that the cause of the fire remained a mystery.

Another fire at Northrepps only three weeks ago caused extensive damage to a sculptor's studio housed in outbuildings at Rectory Road. Police forensic experts investigated the blaze but found no clues.

Det Con Terry Lowe, of Sheringham CID, said yesterday that police were "keeping an open mind" about the cause of Saturday's fire.

"As yet there is nothing to link the three fires which have happened in the village in recent months, but obviously our inquiries are continuing into all three. A fire investigation team has inspected the site of Saturday's fire but has no definite information about its cause," he said.

Anyone with information about any of the fires is asked to telephone Sheringham CID (Sheringham 822121) or contact their nearest police station.

On the left is a poignant shot of a dejected John Golden surveying the wreckage of the 148 year old sawmill shop. To the immediate left is a cutting from the Eastern Daily Press of 22nd May 1989.

Iron and ubiquitous castings

The story of iron

Iron is a remarkable substance. It constitutes about 35% of the mass of the planet, generating the magnetic poles; small traces of the element are needed to sustain life in humans and other species; and its usefulness led ancient man to revere the metal.

Several thousand years ago, people discovered that fire could be used to extract metals from ore, and the process of smelting was born. It is hard to overstate the significance of this step which was to allow mankind to progress to amazing new levels of development. Indeed, some may consider it divinely ordained. We are all familiar with the story of Adam and Eve, the first man and woman, but perhaps not so many of us know that, just a few generations afterwards, God sensibly decided to create the first instructor in iron and brass craftsmanship, Tubal-Cain. Check it out in Genesis 4:22.

Smelting of copper came first, simply because it melts at a lower temperature than iron. That led to the practice of casting: pouring molten metal into a mould to form a particular shape. In this way, copper tools, ornaments and vessels were created. But the big problem was copper's softness: it couldn't take a hard cutting edge. Then, possibly because tin ore (cassiterite) is sometimes found alongside copper ore, the wonders of the alloy bronze came to be discovered. The amalgam of 90% copper and 10% tin was far stronger than either of its constituents, and bronze proved ideal for swords, axes and knives. The use of copper/bronze came to different regions of the world at different times and, as the change arrived – often introduced by trade or military invasion – that particular area moved out of the Stone Age and into the Bronze Age. The ancient Egyptians were one of the first civilisations to employ a primitive charcoal furnace to produce copper and bronze articles; this was around 3,500 BC. Many of their tombs display wall paintings which, sometimes accompanied by a helpful hieroglyphic commentary, explain the procedures. Often these ancient pictograms reveal clear similarities with the basic principles of modern metalworking.

Though Britain was a relative late-comer to bronze technology, the discovery of plentiful supplies of tin ore in Devon and Cornwall allowed the country to become a world-renowned producer of bronze in ancient times.

Just as copper and bronze had supplanted flint and stone in the long march of human development, so eventually iron came to trump bronze. The inhabitants of Cyprus – literally the Copper Island – moved from copper to iron and, soon after 1,000 BC, iron usage spread from Cyprus to the Aegean area, roughly

Carriers of molten metal in John Golden's foundry used a method remarkably akin to that of the workers at an Egyptian copper furnace shown here

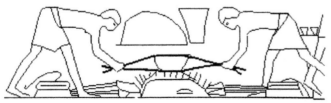

marking the turning point from Bronze Age to Iron Age, though at the time the change would have been gradual and overlapping. Archaeological investigation has revealed widespread use of iron tools and weapons in China by 500 BC, indicating that they employed the basic principle of the blast furnace at that time. In due course, knowledge of these techniques spread to India, Africa and Japan.

Despite the name of the era, craftsmen then worked with more than just iron; many beautiful gold and silver items were produced. And we can't move on without mentioning that it was in Norfolk, near King's Lynn, that a series of digs (intermittently between 1948 and 1989) eventually revealed one of the most celebrated collections of iron-age artefacts: the Snettisham Treasure. Now housed in the British Museum, the hoard of bracelets, coins and other pieces includes 175 stunning silver and gold torc necklaces. These had been made by Iron Age 'barbarians' of the Iceni, the tribe which, a century on, was to be led by Boudica, Norfolk's ferocious warrior queen. But that's another story.

The history of iron-making reflects steady but unremarkable progress punctuated by occasional dramatic leaps forward. If we skip onwards several hundred years, we find one such major advance when, in 1496, the first blast furnace in England was established at Buxted in Sussex. This permitted larger quantities of metal items to be produced compared to the modest output from the smaller more simple furnaces used up to that time. For many years thereafter iron production employed progressively bigger and more effective furnaces, bellows and hammers. The source of heat still came from the charcoal mixed in with the ore. The growing requirements of the military (think of iron cannons and cannon-balls), combined with domestic needs, created an increasing demand for metal production and, since charcoal comes from wood, inevitably this led to the loss of swathes of European forests, with parts of the UK becoming denuded.

Then came another significant advance when, in 1709, Abraham Darby substituted coke for charcoal. Three generations of Darbys – confusingly all given the same first name – were involved in iron-working developments, but it was the first Abraham Darby (Darby I) who made the major step of switching to coke. In his improved furnace he found that he needed to increase the blast of air to burn the coke; also he added limestone, a flux to help form slag and thus remove silica. His intense interest in iron production also led to an improved way of using green sand moulds. He established his new coke-burning blast furnace at Coalbrookdale in Shropshire where 70 years later, in 1779, his grandson (Darby III) designed and built the famous Iron Bridge, a technical marvel of its time and still an impressive structure as part of Ironbridge Gorge Museum complex, now a UNESCO World Heritage Site. Today the famous Aga cooker company operates a working foundry at Coalbrookdale. As with any technological change, it took time for Darby I to make the coke process economically viable but during the eighteenth century the new method was made to work effectively and iron began to be produced in large quantities, a key factor in bringing about the eighteenth-century industrial revolution. Since coke is derived from coal as opposed to timber, the attack on the forests diminished and industrialists instead sought additional supplies of coal. Naturally, this led to a rapid increase in mining activity which, in turn, generated higher demand for pumps. In the mid-eighteenth century the talented Scottish engineer James Watt had patented reliable steam engines and these were used to pump out water – the miners' enemy – and thus improve the productivity of coal mines. Innovation in one area stimulated invention in another.

It was around this same period that the modern cupola –a tall cylindrical furnace – was developed (although a rudimentary form had long been known) to take the pig iron from the main smelting process and subject it to a secondary furnace-heating process which burnt off some of the carbon and allowed the molten metal to be cast in sand moulds of any desired shape. This new process offered the attractions of simplicity, versatility and economy. Sand and clay, the main ingredients for mould-making, are readily available and of low cost. The cupola's inherent adaptability means that it may be used to melt not simply iron but also a wide range of other metals and alloys. Provided it is fed regularly, this type of furnace may be operated continuously, allowing a large number of moulds to be poured. Although in industrialised countries the cupola system now largely has been superseded by more advanced methods such as the electric induction furnace, the underlying principles are still the same as those of the earliest days.

More than a century after his discovery (and after patent expiry), Ransome's chill technique for creating a self-sharpening share remained a selling point, as evidenced by Cornish and Lloyd's 1922 advertisement.

We've all heard how important breakthroughs sometimes occur by accident, and one such fortuitous discovery was made and patented in 1803 by Robert Ransome, who hailed from Norwich and ran a foundry in Ipswich. Based on an earlier patent, Ransome had been producing cast-iron plough-shares for some years when, one fateful day, a mould broke, causing the partially-molten share to spill onto the floor. After spluttering a few curses, the ever-curious Ransome looked more closely at the messy casting on the floor. A careful inspection revealed something intriguing: the part of the share touching the ground had become harder than the rest. The principle of 'chill' had been discovered. John Golden described using this chill technique to produce a hardened surface on certain castings. Ransome's brainwave, however, was to see not only the benefit of having one part of the share hardened through chilling, but also the advantage in allowing the other part to remain relatively soft. Because the blade's soft side wore away faster than the hardened side, the cutting surface constantly re-sharpened itself. As sceptical farmers listened to his initial sales pitch, Ransome's claim must have sounded like wizardry, for he was the first person in the world to offer the self-sharpening plough-share. The Ransome operation grew dramatically and continued well into the twentieth century, becoming widely known for Ransome lawn mowers ('The Best in the World') as well as other products. The business underwent various corporate restructurings but in 1998 was acquired by an overseas company and so ceased to be an independent entity.

The Victorian era, when vast fortunes were made in the second-wave industrial revolution, produced men of outstanding inventiveness, confidence and wealth, and one such was Henry Bessemer, who had the flair to exploit his inventions to his own enormous benefit. One example came when he found that the price of powdered brass – used in calligraphy and artwork – was two hundred times higher than solid brass. Bessemer invented a steam-driven machine to create the powder far more cheaply than the prevailing manual method. Going to great lengths to keep his process secret, his pile of brass powder soon was accompanied by an equally large pile of hard cash.

Bessemer turned his attention to the production of steel, which at the time could be made only in small batches. In essence, steel is just iron with a reduced carbon content. Pig iron coming out of the smelter contains around 4% carbon and this, together with impurities such as manganese, phosphorous, silicon and sulphur, causes it to be brittle. If the carbon level is shrunk to just under 2%, steel is obtained. That may not sound like a big step, but in the nineteenth century achieving that apparently small diminution in carbon was immensely time-consuming and could be carried out only in limited quantities.

Compared to brittle iron, however, steel had far greater potential for large projects such as railway lines and ship-building, and Bessemer saw the huge opportunities – and personal benefit – if only steel could be produced economically on a large scale. Bessemer's theory, which provoked scepticism and indeed incredulity, was that blasts of cold air applied to molten cast iron could be a short-cut conversion method to produce steel, and he set up a demonstration to prove the point. Almost everyone else in the industry thought that cold air blasts would solidify the iron prematurely, precipitating some unimaginable catastrophe. The majority were about to find a simple truth: the prevailing consensus is not always correct. The experiment showed that the air blast caused excess carbon along with impurities to be burnt off, leaving the residual carbon-reduced metal as, more or less, steel. His confidence had been vindicated conclusively and ultimately Bessemer's method proved outstandingly successful. He patented his eponymous converter process in 1856, started up his own firm to exploit his invention and, it is said, made 50% profit on average every month for 14 years. Not surprisingly he became even richer and in 1879 was

awarded a knighthood. In due course, both the Bessemer method and the alternative open-hearth technique were supplanted by the electric arc (1887) and the basic oxygen (1952) processes, with the latter now the most commonly used.

As we have seen, carbon content is critical. Initial smelter output – pig iron –contains between 3.5% and 4.5% carbon. When that is passed through a cupola or similar process, the resultant cast iron has between 2.0% and 4.0% carbon. But when pig iron is put through the powerful converter – the Bessemer or equivalent process – the carbon content is shrunk to less than 2% and that output becomes steel. Generally, steel-making is on a far larger scale than cast-iron production. A steel mill contains both a blast furnace (smelter) to produce pig iron from the raw ore, and alongside it a converter to remove carbon and so change the pig iron into steel.

We've done much to eulogize iron, but to be fair we have to admit that it has its drawbacks. Whilst cast iron has been used to create some notable structures such as the world's first (and still intact) iron bridge over the Severn at Ironbridge, the famous Crystal Palace (destroyed by 1936

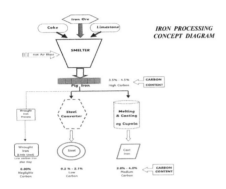

*IRON PROCESSING
CONCEPT DIAGRAM*

fire) and columns for the pier at Cromer, it has also been responsible for some unfortunate failures. Although strong under compression –hence pier columns – cast iron has low tensile strength and so is less reliable for length-wise joists such as girders. Despite its many uses, it is not the best choice for substantial structures. For good reason, designers of large buildings have long favoured steel.

Wrought iron is little produced today. Formerly, it was made in small batches by heating an ore and charcoal mixture to drive off most of the impurities; the residual 'bloom' of porous iron and slag was wrought or beaten by the blacksmith. In the 1780s Henry Cort introduced the 'puddling' method which required the iron and fuel to be kept separate whilst being heated in a reverberatory furnace. Human strength was still called for, as a gang of strong men continuously stirred or puddled the molten metal in order to allow the hot air to circulate through it. In the mid-nineteenth century a number of structures, including Brunel's Albert Bridge at Saltash near Plymouth, were built using wrought iron in preference to cast iron, and these structures, along with other comparative tests, demonstrated the apparent superiority of wrought iron which, with its exceptionally low carbon content, had better malleability.

However, using muscle power for the arduous task of puddling was hardly a great way forward for mankind and, after the advent of large-volume steel-making, a form known as mild steel was used to make most so-called wrought-iron pieces. Occasionally true wrought iron is needed for authentic repairs to ancient structures, and one company continues to specialise in producing 'genuine' wrought iron.

Thousands of years ago, iron was regarded as a precious metal. Today when we consider its widespread applications, it must still be respected as one of the bedrocks of our existence. Iron truly remains a precious metal.

Castings everywhere

Foundry-produced castings are not obscure items, but are to be found in every part of our modern world.

The inside of a Steinway grand piano has its 240 wires (many of the 88 keys having triple strings) and these are held in place by a specially-made harp-shaped frame of iron or steel, cast in Steinway's own foundry. The most talented pianists, in the world's foremost concert halls, depend upon the foundryman's craft.

Walk along any street in the UK and you will see the familiar red pillar box. We take its sturdy presence for granted and yet there's something special about it. Although it can be found in some former overseas

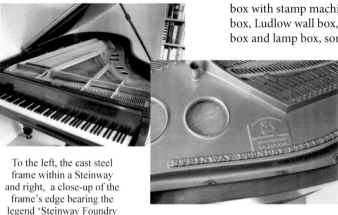

To the left, the cast steel frame within a Steinway and right, a close-up of the frame's edge bearing the legend 'Steinway Foundry Steel Casting'.

territories – for example, the Bahamas – essentially it is a symbol of Britain. To the traveller in a homogenised world, it is an unmistakable and reassuring image that speaks of home. Roadside letter-boxes began to appear in 1852, a decade after the 1840 introduction of the world's first postage stamp. Over the years since then there has been a bewildering variety of designs, sizes and, on brief occasions, alternative materials. There have been the first standard pillar box, second standard pillar box, high fluted pillar box, flattened-top fluted box, Penfold pillar box, vertical-aperture box, dual-aperture box, oval box,

box with stamp machine, standard wall box, Ludlow wall box, free-standing wall box and lamp box, some of which came in larger and smaller sizes and all, since 1887, carrying the cipher of the then reigning monarch. Though often a tall cylindrical red shape, the lamp-box type affixed to a post is also a common sight as we know in our village; Northrepps parish has six, of which three are wall boxes. The other three are lamp-boxes: small, upright rectangular-shaped boxes mounted on a metal pole. Apart from a few trials using substitute materials that any sensible person would deplore, our red friend in all its forms is cast iron. Yes, it's foundry-made.

Another familiar sight, though becoming less common, is the red

telephone box. This elegant beauty was created in 1924 by Sir Giles Gilbert Scott. In the early twentieth century various designs using materials as different as concrete and plywood were tried and found wanting. The best and most suitable design, the K6, uses cast iron. Happily the K6's threatened disappearance has been halted as more local councils recognise its iconic status and take steps to preserve this charming and familiar feature on the streets of our towns and villages. It's reassuring to see that Northrepps retains its red telephone box, another ringing tribute to the skill of the foundryman.

Walk around Cromer and everywhere are examples of the art of casting in iron and other metals. The smart blue benches on the rising coastal path eastwards from town

are good examples of modern foundry work. Walk further in the same direction, however, and we find something altogether more interesting, and relevant to our story.

Strolling in Happy Valley, it would be easy

to walk past the modest bench lacking a backrest, but it represents a small piece of local industrial history, for the metal supports are early examples of cast iron produced by Randell's. Look carefully and it's possible to make out the legend on the cast-iron end-piece: F Randell Ltd, North Walsham. This is the company which at one time owned Northrepps' foundry.

As we go about our daily life, unwittingly we go over, alongside and under foundry products: drainage gratings, manhole covers, railings, bollards and street signs.

Visit an older house or perhaps a National Trust property and there will be another slew of cast iron pieces: guttering, hoppers, downpipes, gates, wall tie-plates, door knockers, radiators, weather vanes and air-brick grills.

Return home and more examples of the foundryman's craft surround us: house sign or plaque, garden furniture, umbrella stand, fire grate and fire-back, bed-frame, bath-tub, towel rail and roof-lights. And in the kitchen, just think about the favourite cooking vessel of your mother or grandmother – surely that grand old cast-iron pot? And what about that acme of middle-class aspiration, the Aga cooker?

In the mid-nineteenth century, Cromer had about 50 local crab-boats. The metal base for a crab/lobster pot comes from a foundry. Crab-pot bases were amongst the items produced by John Golden's Northrepps operation.

Switch on the radio or TV and you may hear the unmistakable sound of Big Ben

Base plates or 'musics' of the Cromer and Sheringham crab pots were made at Golden's foundry

tolling the hour. Although commonly applied to the entire clock tower, strictly the name Big Ben refers only to the grand bell which was created in a foundry specialising in bell manufacture: the Whitechapel Bell Foundry established in 1570 in London's East End. Big Ben first rang out in 1859.

Let's not forget our own Northrepps church bells; all eight foundry-cast. The official notice shows that the earliest bell was cast in 1626 and the most recent in 1981.

Two of the most ancient bells in Norfolk are those of Anmer Church on the Sandringham estate. The bells, restored

St. Mary the Virgin			Northrepps, Norfolk	
Treble.	Taylor	1981	3 - 1 - 11	
2.	Taylor	1981	3 - 2 - 21	
3.	Taylor	1938	4 - 0 - 23	
4.	Warner	1872	4 - 0 - 13	
5.	unknown		5 - 2 - 16	
6.	J. Brend	1636	7 - 3 - 8	
7.	Warner	1872	8 - 2 - 25	
Tenor.	W. & A. Brend	1626	11 - 1 - 0	

Tenor in D

The peal was augmented to eight in 1981.

The church notice for the bells of Northrepps church

at Whitechapel during 2012, were cast originally in Norwich in 1420 and 1573 respectively.

Sailors have keel, ballast weight, slipway rollers, propellers, bow caps, shoes, pivots, tiller arms and clamps.

Enter the industrial world and the dependence on castings is widespread: gear case, flywheel, angle plate, pump body, valve, crank shaft, cylinder head, machine tools and yokes. Many more cast iron

parts than could be listed here are used in industries such as valve-making, mining, earth-moving equipment, oil and gas exploration and automobile production. Norfolk means agriculture and that provides more examples of castings: shear blades, plough, harrow, rolls, press wheels and plough points.

Even in the world of arts and entertainment, castings reign supreme. Amid the frippery and floss of the Oscar ceremony, many might consider the most

solid and sensible thing present to be the statuette held aloft by the overwhelmed recipient. Similarly, in the UK the Bafta mask statuette, looking like a face on a stick, is made at New Pro Foundries in West London.

Famous sculptors such as Auguste Rodin, Henry Moore and Barbara Hepworth used a variety of materials, ranging from stone to clay, to create their famous works, and in a number of cases they employed casting techniques to make metal versions, though usually in bronze rather than iron.

The guardians of Trafalgar Square are the four huge foundry-produced lions, designed by Sir Edwin Landseer. At the Old Bailey, the famous Lady Justice with sword and scales is foundry-made. And of course the world-famous Eros statute in Piccadilly Circus was also cast – in aluminium – in a foundry. The military have long used castings for artillery gun parts; in past centuries cannon and cannon-balls were cast iron. And in more recent times cast ejector-seat pins have been used in Hawk trainer jets. Another more sinister application was recently discovered lodged in the thick mud of the Thames: a well-preserved ball and chain made of cast iron. The unfortunate seventeenth-century prisoner would never have escaped from his heavy iron manacle without the key.

Iron, casting and smith work have been so important in our past that our language is full of allusions; the old literary phrases remain common currency, used often without conscious thought as to their true origin.

To convey urgency, we strike while the iron is hot. To eliminate annoyances, we iron out the creases, but if we attempt too much, we may have too many irons in the fire. And when we need to illustrate toughness in our leaders, the iron metaphor is the most vivid: the Iron Duke; the Iron Chancellor; the Iron Lady; all of whom, naturally, ruled with a rod of iron, though sometimes they used an iron fist in the velvet glove, and invariably they were steely-faced. An especially nasty medieval method of despatching enemies was the Iron Maiden. At the start of railway expansion the synonym for train, particularly in the USA, was the iron horse. In the nineteenth century, a warship was an ironclad. In twentieth-century wartime, soldiers ate iron rations, after which they may have given the enemy cold steel. The German army's highest award was the Iron Cross. In a speech in Missouri in 1946, Winston Churchill memorably declared that 'an iron curtain has descended across the Continent [of Europe]'. And wherever they may now live, Scots recall their other national drink: Irn Bru - 'made in Scotland from girders'.

The sources of most everyday items in our world are obvious: groceries from farmers and fishermen; fabrics and clothing from weaving, knitting and dyeing, buildings from concrete, brick and glass, and furniture from trees. Yet too often the myriad of cast metal items in thousands of places and structures seems not to register in popular comprehension. Despite the allusions deep in our everyday language, and in spite of the crucial role it plays in every aspect of life, the foundry business often is taken for granted. Yet we cannot exist without its multifaceted contribution to civilization. It deserves stronger recognition, for it holds our world together.

Wheelwright and cartwright

If any painting epitomises the popular perception of England in the early nineteenth century it is surely John

Constable's *The Hay Wain*, painted in 1821. Constable based this view on a site near Flatford on the river Stour in Suffolk, the adjoining county to Norfolk, and the picture conveys a feeling not just of time but of place: of East Anglia. The rustic cottage, the gentle river, the flat green meadow all add to that feeling of rural tranquillity. But, true to its title, the chief subject is the cart or wain. And more than that, it is the wheel of the wain that seems to act as a focus, drawing the gaze as though towards a target. Constable had paid attention to his focal subject, with the hub, the spokes, the segmented felloe or circular rim and the iron outer tyre all painted in meticulous detail; almost, it might be imagined, as a tribute to the skill of the wheelwright who created the appealing symmetry and strength of the hay wain's timber wheels.

The word 'wright' is an old English term meaning worker and descriptions such as wainwright and cartwright live on as English surnames.

The wheelwright's craft properly belongs to the horse-drawn period, and within the Golden family at Northrepps it was George Golden who, around 1860, first used his carpenter's training to expand into the specialised area of the wheelwright. In the 1870s, as well as wheels for carts and carriages George made wooden wheels, both large and small, for the 'ordinary' bicycle (known after its demise in the 1890s as the penny-farthing). As time went by,

Constable's Haywain, reproduced by kind permission of The National Gallery, London

George's wheelwright's skills were passed to his son, Frank. During that period, before motorised transport had become commonplace, the Goldens were also cartwrights, building wagons, carts and tumbrils for farmers in different parts of Norfolk.

One of just a few surviving accounting documents is an invoice issued by Frank Golden for work done for Mr R. Cooper at

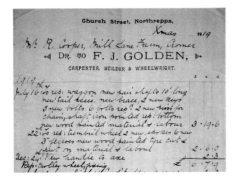

Mill Lane Farm, Cromer. Frank's charges include wagon repairs carried out on 16th July 1919, new spokes and new three-inch felloe segments fitted to a tumbrel (or tumbril) wheel on 22nd July. With other matters, the total is six pounds five shillings and nine pence or £6.27.

Another document of interest, bringing together wheelwright and foundry, is a letter of 11th July 1919 to Frank Golden

from T. W. Burton, the firm which, in the late nineteenth and early twentieth century, owned and operated the new Church Street foundry in Northrepps. We see the closing reference to Mr Shepheard holding Smithy Notes; this could be a request for mild-steel bars for the blacksmith who assisted Frank in his wheelwright work, or might relate to other metal items for building jobs. Clearly the content of the letter is more important than the typing accuracy.

In 1919 John Golden joined his father to train as a carpenter and progressively also learned the skills of wheelwrighting. Father and son, together with their employees, were kept busy building, repairing,

tightening and re-tyring wooden wheels throughout the 1920s and part of the 1930s. As with all agricultural activities, the intensity of work depended on the seasons, and the period between hay-making and corn harvest, when carts might stand idle in the hot weather, was the peak time for repair and renewal of wheels. John recalls one particular month in the 1920s when they had to deal with the remarkable total of 400 carts of varying types and sizes, all requiring maintenance of some sort. Eventually, in the mid-1930s, the rubber tyre arrived and demand for wheelwright work started to diminish noticeably, though it never ceased totally. According to John, the business had continued to make a limited number of wooden wheels right up to the early 1940s, but the war brought rapid change and by the late 1940s almost all agricultural carts were fitted with rubber tyres.

Even up to the early 1980s a few customers continued to ask John to carry out wheel work, but this was only for those with specialist collections who appreciated having the skill of an authentic wheelwright applied to their treasured carts. And in that same period, John claimed that it would have been possible to find a few Golden-

At Northrepps wheelwright's shop, a wheel made with a rope felloe and the clamp used to secure the ends of the rope.

built carts still in use on local farms.

In his later years, John was fond of demonstrating, to anyone who expressed an interest, the techniques employed in making a wheel. In this bygone world of horse-drawn carts, the word tyre means a metal rim; we must forget rubber.

The wheelwright work brought together several skills. In the carpenters' shop at the sawmill, the main timber work –hub, spokes and felloe – was carried out. Across the road in the foundry site, the blacksmith would make the metal tyre and then the final wheelwright task was to furnace-heat the tyre which would be fitted over the wooden frame.

The north-east section of the quadrangle of buildings – the present kitchen – was the wheelwright shop, and beyond it, to the north-west, stood a separate building which housed the tyre furnace, stabling and gig-house.

The gig/stable/tyre building has since been demolished.

Wheelwrighting was much more than just slotting some pieces together like self-assembly furniture. The craftsman needed to understand the purpose of the cart, to assess where and how stress forces would apply, and then to form a judgement about the types of timber for the component parts. Only well-seasoned wood would be used, and a rule of thumb was to allow one year of seasoning for each inch of thickness. The strength of a cart-wheel depended, above all, on the sound

workmanship of its wooden hub, otherwise known as the nave or stock. Usually the hub would be cut from elm, whose tight cross-grain provided even tension all round. After being turned on the lathe, the sockets or mortices into which the spokes are driven must be cut out at the correct angle so that the spokes are all inclined slightly forward, giving the wheel the hint of a concave shape. This causes the spoke to be absolutely upright when at the bottom of the turn, but to lean fractionally outward in its uppermost position. This arrangement means that the thrust of the load is exactly on the centre of the arch made by every pair of spokes at the nave. A concave wheel alignment also matches the cart-shape which usually was wider at the top and narrower at the base. The spokes themselves invariably would be constructed from oak. The felloes or outer rim, created in segments, would be made from elm, ash or beech.

The wheelwright also had to be a skilled carpenter, for the various wooden pieces would be jointed together without screws or nails. Technical understanding could be critical. For example, chamfering, or shaving away, of the inner angles of wheel felloes actually adds to their strength, by

The wheel of this cart at Gressenhall Museum illustrates the outward lean and concave shape created by the spokes. This dish shape helps protect the nave/hub which, were it to protrude further, might sustain damage which could break the whole wheel.

equalising the thickness of wood where it is cut through for the spokes with the thickness between these holes, and so distributing the strain along the whole circumference. The choice of timber, the shape of the hub and the style of woodworking were unique to each job, and the skilled wheelwright, when asked to repair an old wheel, often could read much of its origins and history from a careful examination of the materials and workmanship.

Before the blacksmith could start his task of making the tyre, he needed to know the required length of metal. This was done using a trammel (or 'traveller'), which was something like a miniature version of the rod-and-wheel used by surveyors to measure distance along the ground.

After marking a chalk start-point on both the wooden wheel and the trammel, the wheelwright would run the circular trammel along the outer rim of the wheel.

The boring machine used in Northrepps carpenters' shop to bore the centre of the wooden hub.

By counting the number of turns (or part-turns), the length of the circumference could readily be calculated. The blacksmith would select a suitable length of flat-bar mild steel, usually three inches wide, which would be heated and then passed through the tyre bender, a machine with three rollers. As the rollers were turned, the metal bar was forced to curve as it passed through. Repeating this procedure caused the bar gradually to become a complete circle. Generally the blacksmith would begin with some extra length to allow for an overlap, and put a temporary fix in place. This preliminary metal hoop was compared with the wooden wheel lying flat on the ground on the iron wheel-plate. The aim was to get the cold metal circumference about half-an-inch shorter than the wooden wheel. Once satisfied with the measurement, the blacksmith would weld the join into its final position. Now it was time to use the tyre furnace (or oven), a narrow brick structure located at one end of the gig-house/stable building. Open at the front, and with a small chimney on top, the furnace height was six feet (nearly two metres), but its width was restricted to about 12 inches (30 cm), forcing the tyre to remain upright during heating. Using kindling and whatever else came to hand, a fire was started and, once established, the metal tyre was rolled into the flames. The wooden wheel was resting on the ground nearby, on the iron wheel-plate. When the tyre was judged to have been heated sufficiently, two men pulled it out of the oven and, using long metal gripes, carried it to the wheel-plate and placed it over the wooden wheel. Using hammers, they tapped around the metal rim, being careful not to over-hit one side or the other. Once securely in place, the tyre was doused with buckets of cold water. The contraction of the metal tightened the whole structure into a secure finished wheel. Finally, as an additional precaution, hand-made nails would be driven into the wooden felloe through pre-cut holes in the metal tyre.

Above is the tyre bending machine, surrounded by weeds. On the right is the tyre oven and below Bill Pardon and John Golden fit a tyre.

Wheels made and repaired by John and his workers were used in a wide range of products. The photograph, dated 16th September 1969 (when John was 64 years old) shows a large-wheeled single-row root drill.

At the top, John making a new wheel to match the original, damaged wheel seen in the picture below it. It is possible this was for the gypsy caravan. On the left is a Victorian trammel for measuring the tyre's circumference.

One event illustrates John's great interest in and knowledge of wheelwright matters. In 1971, in the Northrepps wheelwright shop, John Golden worked on a pair of replacement wheels for a gypsy caravan. Remarkably, by examining the hub of one of the rotting wheels he was replacing, he was able to tell that the caravan had begun its days at Chardstock in Devon in 1892. Now that's real detective work.

Above, the hot tyre is hammered home and, left, cold water ensures the tyre tightens its grip on the wooden structure. Below is a wheelwright bench at Northrepps.

WAGON RESTORED

MR. JOHN GOLDEN (seated) and Mr. William Pardon who have rebuilt an old Corona soft drinks wagon at Northrepps.

THE demand for horse-drawn wagons and carts must almost be non-existent now, but Mr. John Golden, of Northrepps, has recently been involved in the restoration of an old wagon for the Corona soft drinks firm.

Mr. Golden, who used to make such carts in earlier days, discovered two old Corona wagons on a Norfolk farm. Although they were in poor condition he was able to save various

North Norfolk
NOTEBOOK

parts, and from these he rebuilt the new wagon.

"All the woodwork is new and the wheels had to be sent away," Mr. Golden explained.

Corona have arranged for the wagon to be taken to Wales where it will be hand painted in its original style.

Mr. R. H. Failes, sales manager at Norwich for Corona, explained that the freshly-painted wagon would be returned to Norwich in May for a county athletics meeting to take place at Lakenham. "Corona are sponsoring the athletics and I imagine that the wagon will be used to sell drinks from," he said.

Retaining the interest generated by his father in cartwright work, John would get hold of old carts with the aim of restoring them to their former authentic condition. Though the carts were of little use to him, invariably there would be a story behind each, and this was the real attraction. Provenance won over practicality.

An article in the *North Norfolk News* on 30th April 1976 recounted the story of John's discovery, restoration and return of a Corona horse-drawn cart. The original Corona Soft Drinks Company had been acquired by Beecham's and later sold on to Britvic. Some loyal and diligent customers claim that bottles of pop bearing the Corona name may still be found.

A decade later, another newspaper report shows that even at 81 John professed an interest in finding and restoring any cart with an intriguing history. This time the origin of the handcart lay with the Chivers jam-making family. According to John, Chivers originally dealt only in fruit sales, and in the nineteenth century had used the cart to take fruit from their Cambridgeshire base to the local market. The Chivers family had owned a holiday home in Overstrand and the cart had been sent there after the business had changed from fruit sales to jam making. In 1986 John paid £100 to rescue the 1893 cart from the Overstrand garden.

It is not clear whether John completed his restoration of the Chivers handcart. In any event, John died less than three years after acquiring the cart which, several

array of miscellaneous items, from top hats to a croquet set, were sold at auction. The first sale, held at the Old Foundry, offered some carts, wheels and miscellaneous equipment. The second sale, a month later, was held in Northrepps Village Hall, where carts, carriages, ploughs, furniture, books, magazines and various other strange and wonderful items went under the hammer. Amongst the sale items, those relating to John's wheelwright and cartwright business were:

- Governess Cart
- Pony Trap
- Two-wheel Builder's Cart
- Two-wheel Market Trader's Cart
- Costermonger's two-wheel Market Barrow
- Dealer's and Other Hand-carts
- Invalid Carriage
- Phaeton (for restoration)
- Builder's Wagonette
- Four-wheel and two-wheel horse-drawn timber drags
- Twenty individual wheels (for wagon, gig and trap)
- Pair of wagon wheels with rope felloes
- Hand-cranked iron tyre bender
- Wheelwright's hand-cranked hub borer

years later, appeared as one of the items auctioned off by his widow in 1995.

As an inveterate collector, John Golden accumulated a wide range of carts, wagons and the like, as well as individual wheels.

After John's death in 1989, his widow, Mary, promptly auctioned off his collection of vintage cars, but allowed his carts and wheels to remain in store for more than six years. Then, on two separate dates in 1995, all the carts, together with an astonishing

The wheels of history . . .

A North Norfolk collector has unearthed a Victorian fruit handcart which he plans to restore to its former glory.

Mr John Golden, of Church Street, North-repps, bought the cart for £100 from the garden of the holiday home of the Chivers jam-making family in Overstrand.

The cart is dated 1893 and Mr Golden believes it was used to take fruit to market from Histon in Cambridgeshire, where the Chivers were based. He said it had been moved to Overstrand about 90 years ago and was used in the garden.

Apparently the Chivers family used to sell fruit in Cambridge markets until on one occasion they could not achieve a good price.

So instead of selling the fruit they decided to become jam makers — and did not regret the idea.

The company was certainly a big concern by the early 20th century as Kelly's Directory for 1908 bears out.

Part of the entry for Histon reads: "Messrs. Chivers and Sons Ltd. who own several hundred acres of fruit gardens in the parish have a large jam factory in the village, in which they employ over 1000 people."

The directory went on: "The works are lighted with electricity and provided with a large artesian well, capable of supplying a tank with 20,000 gallons of water in six hours."

All this technology meant that the factory was able to produce 100 tons of jam a day.

MR John Golden, of Northrepps, with the Chivers handcart he intends to restore.

Also up for sale was the star of the show, a large horse-drawn railway wagon, so unusual that the *Eastern Daily Press* had run a feature on it some days before the auction. It was a low-slung black-painted cart, almost eighteen feet (over 5 m) long, which had once belonged to the London Midland & Scottish railway company. Thought to date from 1895, it had a low floor, deep sides and leaf-spring suspension, and carried the identification number 628. The wagon had been restored by John Golden, but neither Mary Golden nor the auctioneer could say where it had come from, though other sources indicate that it had been used to transport sheep from market to outlying farms. The EDP article invited anyone with additional information to contact the auctioneer. No records are available to show who purchased this huge wagon nor, indeed, any of the other items. Perhaps LMS wagon No 628 today sits in some collector's yard, intermittently admired by enthusiasts.

Despite its poor quality, this photograph gives an indication of the unusual characteristics and size of the LMS cart.

Undertaker

Death is big business. In twenty-first century Britain there are over 600,000 deaths each year, and the market is worth around £1 billion. Scan the financial pages in any reputable newspaper and you can find, within the professional and support services section of the share-price listings, a public company whose main activity is operating funeral homes and crematoriums and whose annual revenue exceeds £260 million. The quoted company's immense size has been achieved mainly through the acquisition of many smaller funeral parlours, but the parent company operates by retaining and publicising the original local names. At a time of distress we need to be supported by those we know, and when it comes to funeral arrangements it is natural to want to deal with people who are aware of local circumstances and will act with the sensitivity that we feel, however unfairly, may be lacking in a large organisation. Big feels impersonal, whereas small and local gives comfort. And small and local is just how the Golden funeral business was a century ago.

Throughout human history there have been elaborate rituals associated with funerals, particularly those of high-status members of a tribe or hierarchy. Discoveries of the burial places of Iron Age chieftains often reveal a body surrounded by extravagant possessions: gold, silver and ornate pieces of cloth.

In the seventeenth century, a series of Burial in Woollen Acts between 1667 and 1814 required the dead (apart from plague victims) to be buried in pure English woollen shrouds. No other type of textile was permitted, and a relative had to provide an affidavit, sworn in front of a JP, attesting to adherence; non-compliance resulted in a £5 fine (about £700 in today's money). Some, especially ladies, made provision for the £5 to be paid so that they might be buried in their finery. The Acts, which were simply a way of supporting the indigenous woollen industry, eventually fell into disrepute and were widely ignored after 1770 as fashion and greater affluence made coffins increasingly popular. One source suggests that the practice of securing the body by knotting the woollen shroud at either end gave rise to the expression 'get knotted' whose meaning originally was 'to die'.

In the early nineteenth century, the clergyman dealt with the entire burial ritual with the sexton digging the grave in the churchyard. Maintaining an accurate record of those buried in the local churchyard depended on the thoroughness of the parish clerk. As we read elsewhere, John Golden's grandfather, George Golden, had been parish clerk in the latter part of the nineteenth century, though by 1837 the registration of deaths had become a civil matter in England. At that time the concept of an undertaker or funeral director did not exist, and it was only in the late nineteenth century that these titles and professional duties became more common.

As churchyards became overcrowded, the Act of 1853 permitted ratepayers to elect a Board with powers to buy land for a cemetery, and such separate burial grounds are evident in many towns and villages today. Simple arithmetic, however, points to further pressure on the use of scarce land. In the mid to late nineteenth century there was an increasing interest in and, it appears, some practice of, disposing of the dead by cremation – the UK's first declared (modern) cremation being carried out in 1885 in Woking, Surrey – although at national level it became formally legal only with the Crematorium Act 1902. Today, 72% of British people choose to be cremated. Moreover, eco-friendly or 'natural' funerals are becoming more common, with some choosing to be buried in a vertical space-saving position and, in a curious echo of seventeenth-century practice, favouring a biodegradable shroud rather than being entombed in a wooden coffin.

One custom in Victorian times, continuing into the early twentieth century in some regions, was the baking of funeral biscuits. Shortcake, ladies' fingers and caraway-flavoured biscuits would be distributed as an invitation to a funeral. Also in the nineteenth century, some people developed a fear of being confined in a coffin whilst still alive, and this led to various quixotic inventions such as a cord attached to a bell.

The Victorians made much of the funeral rituals, though in the matter of death there was a considerable difference between town and country. In the city equality in the eyes of God was not matched by equality in the eyes of man, with the rich and famous having a grand, almost sumptuous, send-off whereas the poor were despatched in a more austere manner. Gradually, however, subtle changes took place as the wealthy felt it appropriate to scale down the flamboyance and at the same time ordinary folk tried to become a little more elaborate and dignified.

In the rural areas, though, there was always a stronger sense of everyone knowing – and grieving with – everyone else, and accordingly most village funerals avoided extremes of rich or poor display and simply followed local tradition and practice. In the late nineteenth and early twentieth centuries, rustic life was insular and villagers had little inclination or opportunity to venture further afield. Of necessity, life – and death – remained parochial. As wooden coffins came to be used more often, it was natural for villagers to ask the local carpenter, the man who could create almost anything out of wood, to make them. Since the carpenter knew the local vicar and employed men who might act as bearers, it made sense for him to offer a full undertaker's service. And so Frank Golden added that to his list of skills.

Frank knew all the villagers and dealt with funerals sensitively, though at the same time he took a commercial view of matters, and the business made a useful contribution to overall profits, not least because this type of work is regular and not much affected by economic cycles. And it was another use for the sawmill's capital-intensive machinery.

Then as now, the cost of a funeral could be a significant expense. Around 1900, it is unlikely that many rural workers earned even a pound a week. Following a death, the surviving relative, who may have had only meagre savings, had to pay a funeral cost equivalent to several weeks' wages. Sometimes, but not always, poorer people took out special insurance to cover the expense of the funeral, and in 1900 the Prudential had twelve million such policies (with an accumulated fund of £17m) for an average weekly premium of two pence (1p). Decades later, in the 1940s, when the welfare state was established, one of the benefits then introduced was a burial grant to help with the funeral cost.

We have some pages from Frank Golden's 1898 cash payments book to give us a clue to some of the expenses then arising. In the part reproduced here, the entry for 27th September 1898 shows a total of £1 7s 6d (£1.37) being paid to the clergyman, clerk and bearers. Since this was a business outgoing, we may assume that the client would have been charged a higher fee. And, of course, on top of that, there was the cost of the coffin, hearse, flowers and other necessary incidentals; the total would have come to several pounds.

For many years the undertaker side was regarded simply as a useful adjunct to the main focus of the Golden business. As already mentioned, the undertaker description had come to be accepted only gradually and, perhaps as a hangover from that attitude, it was the 1930s before the role began to be recognised as important in its own right. In 1933, Kelly's Directory for the first time recorded Frank Golden's activities as undertaker as well as builder and wheelwright. Despite this recognition, Frank didn't feel it necessary to amend the sub-headings on his stationery for some years. The 1939 handwritten invoice/receipt for the funeral of villager Mrs Harriet Dennis (whose executor was Herbert Woodhouse, one of the village grocers) shows how Frank was careful to detail everything, from embossed flannel with frilling to the mortuary charge. As we see, the total cost including the oak coffin with brass plate, bearers' and church

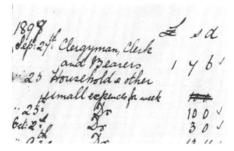

fees and hire of hearse came to £11.00. At that time, a receipt was legally valid only if postage stamps of the appropriate value were gummed in place and cancelled by over-writing. In modern times the average cost of a funeral (including headstone) is £7,622.

In the 1950s the undertaker service provided by John Golden tended to follow the practice set by his father Frank some decades earlier. When advised of a death in the village, John or a colleague would go to the house, speak with the widow or widower and record in the coffin notebook details of the proposed arrangements and the coffin size. Often he would help take the deceased out of the bed and place them on a special board positioned between two chairs. In those days every village had a lady who helped with birth

and death, and John would ask her to attend to wash, tidy and lay out the body.

As it happens, one of the few Golden documents still existing is the coffin notebook used from 1950 to 1958; its pages show personal details and dimensions, with helpful diagrams. To some this may appear ghoulish, but we need to remind ourselves that the bereaved are given freedom to grieve partly because someone else deals with the practicalities in a sensitive but businesslike way.

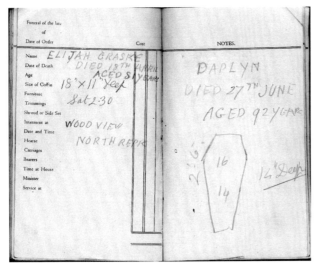

In the sawmill was a pile of planks one inch (25 mm) thick already cut from fallen oak gathered from hedgerows or local plantations. John once remarked, 'I must be one of the few men in Norfolk who, when he makes a coffin, saws out his own planks from a tree.' A number of these rough planks, each two feet (60 cm) wide, would be selected and passed through the planing machine. Any woodyard worker within hearing immediately knew what was being made because the bigger plank caused the electric machine to labour as it planed the unusually large pieces. Sometimes another type of timber – sycamore or chestnut – would be used for the floor of the coffin.

The planed oak planks were finished by hand with scraper and sandpaper; polish was not used. The distinctive bend about a third of the way along the side-pieces was achieved by making six partial vertical cuts and then pouring over a kettleful of boiling water. With the side-panel wood sufficiently softened, it was pressed into the typical slight curved shape. In John's time, each coffin was tailor-made for the person concerned.

From a container on the workshop stove, hot melted pitch was poured into the coffin and spread evenly over the bottom, covering timber joints, and pushed about three inches (7.5 cm) up the sides. The pitch dried rapidly, after which sawdust or shavings to a depth of one inch were spread over the floor of the container. This in turn was covered with a lining cloth tacked to the floor to give a pincushion effect. Extra shavings would be used at one end to create a pillow shape under the cloth covering. In similar fashion, the sides would also be lined with material. Finally, white frilling would be pinned all the way round the top edge. On a wood off-cut, John or a carpenter would write the coffin dimensions; this size-guide later would be handed to the gravedigger. An experienced man such as Walter Hurn or Bill Pardon could make a coffin in a day, though Bill declared it his least favourite job.

Normally the coffin was made during the day and, in the early evening, taken to the house where the best room would have been made ready. The deceased person would be laid in the coffin which was left open so that friends and neighbours might call to pay their respects. Every effort would be made to keep the room cool, and often there was a saucer of milk and a peeled onion to help keep the air fresh. It would be years before this practice was supplanted by the introduction of a Chapel of Rest on the funeral director's premises.

John would check on the body from time to time, and advise when the showing had to be stopped. The burial took place usually within three or four days of death. Typically the coffin would be closed in the morning and the burial carried out later the same day.

It is said that John, whether in or out of public view, always was most respectful and reverential at these times and was a great support to the bereaved whose natural grief often was combined with an overriding feeling of isolation.

The funeral generally required four bearers who would be drawn from John's team of bricklayers, carpenters and retired workers. If the deceased lived close to the church, the coffin would be pushed along the street on a wheeled bier with a bearer at each corner. In more complicated situations, a motorised hearse would be hired from the Cromer coach company used by all villages in the area.

Occasionally John would adapt one of his two Austin 16s to transport an empty coffin to the deceased's home. This unusual mission required removal of the whole of the back seat and the boot lid.

The old manor house had for a long period been divided in two, and its two separate 'front doors' are still apparent. At that time the Goldens lived in one half of the property with the other half shut off.

Occasionally, when the need arose, the closed-off section of the house would be used as an unofficial short-term mortuary.

In an interview in the 1980s, John recalled how his father had told him that in 1916, during an epidemic in the area, one local man, aged about forty-five, had wandered over to watch Frank put the finishing touches to a coffin. 'You'll be making mine next,' said the villager. Within a week he was dead.

By the mid-1950s, the typical cost of a Golden-made coffin including the services

John's two Austin 16s, sometime coffin carriers, were caught up in the destruction caused by the 1989 fire in the timber-yard.

of four bearers and a gravedigger, plus church fees, had increased to £27. It was said that, at that time, Southrepps offered what it considered to be a more upmarket package for around £32. Presumably the end result was the same.

When the grave was dug, the depth was determined by whether a spouse was expected to follow in due course. A double-decker grave would be seven feet (2.1 m) deep, whereas a single version was five feet nine inches (1.75 m). Today the typical grave is not so deep, yet it must be sufficient to allow for the recommended minimum of one metre of soil on top. The 1950s gravedigger received £1.50 for dig and in-fill.

In days gone by, when a notable Northrepps figure died, local tradition dictated that the body, surrounded by lit candles, be left overnight in the church.

On one occasion, John was asked if it wasn't an unhappy sort of profession. 'Unhappy?' he queried, 'What's the bother about that?' During his time as village undertaker, it is estimated that there might have been about 30 burials in a typical year. In some weeks John would deal with two or three funerals; in other weeks there would be none.

Church

Away from work, John regularly attended Northrepps parish church, following in the footsteps not only of his father Frank, but also of his grandfather George who had been parish clerk for many years. The Church of St Mary the Virgin, to give it its full name, is a fine building dating from the 15th century, though a church had stood on the site for hundreds of years before then, going back earlier than 1066.

Let us consider some carpentry and foundry items in the church. The ancient decorated rood screens, which separate nave and chancel, were given to the church

in 1460 by John Playford and his (first) wife Custance whose names are carved on the central band. Apart from a period when the screens were removed (they were later found and reinstated) they have stood for centuries. And for that same length of time, within the delicate tracery, there are at least two tiny faces putting out their tongues at the assembled congregation; a carpenter's mischievous joke from half a millennium ago.

The church tower, almost 90 feet (27 m) high, holds eight bells, two dating from the early seventeenth century, and all made in specialised foundries.

The faces with sticky-out tongues may be seen by personal inspection but are barely discernible from a photograph of the Playford-donated rood screens.

In 1927, at the age of 21, John was elected people's churchwarden, while at the same time Christopher Gurney (father of Joe, Hugh, Pam and Anthony Gurney) was elected Rector's warden. Although neither could have known it then, the two were to remain as wardens for a record 42 years, though John's own term as churchwarden was to stretch well beyond even that.

From time to time the Goldens, Frank and John, presented the church with various artefacts and panels they had constructed using their carpentry skills. In 1940, when Frank was 69 and John 35, the parish newsletter carried the following announcement:

> A gift to the Church. You will have noticed the handsome new notice board in Northrepps Churchyard, made by Mr F. Golden and Mr J. Golden. Mr Golden Snr has told me they wish to make a present of it to the church in memory of his father,

Mr George Golden, who was for 30 years clerk of the parish and died in 1900. We are very grateful to them for their most generous and useful gift.

The notice-board stood near the main gates for 72 years, but eventually succumbed to wood-rot; in May 2012 it was replaced by a new one similar in design to the old. An equally sad fate overtook John's metal weather-vane which he presented to the church to commemorate the 1953 coronation. The wind vane was made of gilded copper and bore the stylised shape of the famous Gallas Plough together with the EIIR monogram and a crown. Fixed to the flag-pole, the vane stood proudly for many decades on top of the tower until one night the pole snapped under the force of a storm; the remnants of the vane were gathered up and now lie discarded in a dark corner.

Mention of a vane reminds us that, in Iron Age England, it was believed that the cock gave protection against thunderstorms, which is why cocks are still to be found on many church steeples, and why they are known as weathercocks.

In 1951 Frank and Pattie were due to celebrate their golden wedding on

John's intricately-made copper wind-vane with crown, plough and royal cipher in celebration of the Queen's coronation.

23rd April, and to mark the occasion Frank, then aged 80, decided to make a table for the church. This was to be no ordinary table, but one made from part of the ancient oak beams which had been removed from the belfry in 1937 and retained in the Golden woodyard. Back in the sixteenth and seventeenth centuries, oak was commonly used for church roofs and cottages throughout East Anglia as well as for the vessels of the English navy, and when Northrepps' original bell frame was constructed in 1626, oak had been the natural choice. Thus a 50-year personal anniversary was to be marked by a 325-year-old piece of oak, fashioned by Frank (with help from Bill Pardon) into a handsome item of furniture.

The table is still in regular use. It is a solid well-worked piece, attactive and utilitarian. Had we been in Frank's place, surely many of us would have opted for an inscription like 'Frank and Pattie 50 years'; yet, if we reflect, that would have betrayed a touch of vanity. Frank didn't care for such self-indulgence. Like the

Frank Golden working on the church table in his carpentry shop. A framed copy of this photograph is displayed on the table in the church.

The completed table – made from oak now almost 400 years old.

One of Frank's oak stools. Underneath the top (below) is carved his initials and the date 1951.

Nurse Golden and her motorbike and (below) the Nurse Golden table. The lower photo shows some of the more recent panels expertly carved by John Golden for Northrepps church.

true craftsman he was, his thought was for the splendour of the material he worked on, and so on the leading edge of the table he carved the legend: MADE FROM THE OLD BELL FRAME. Yet justifiable pride in workmanship required somewhere the identifying mark of the carpenter. Almost out of sight, along the base of one leg, is carved his name 'F J Golden' and on the other leg 'Me Fecit et Dedit MCMLI' ('Made and given by me 1951'). The table's attractive and sturdy lines, the reference to its provenance, the maker's unassuming claim discreetly couched in Latin and the item's sensible usefulness all attest to the skill and modesty of the man who, at 80, wanted to create a special piece of furniture which would return the ancient oak to his local church.

As an interesting footnote to Frank's anniversary table, we find that he used some off-cuts from the same bell-frame oak to make three small stools. One was given to Pattie's relatives, the Copeman family, another to the Fish family (and still owned by parish councillor Lorna Fish), and the third given to the Harrison family for whom Frank and John had built a house in Nut Lane.

Just a few metres from Frank's large oak table stands another table; a small modest item, easily overlooked. The curious visitor may read on its base-plate 'In memory of M E Golden from friends at Church Street Northrepps' but feel none the wiser. Its story, briefly, is this. Mary Ethel Fuller, born in Paston in 1896, was one of nine children of a cowman, Adam, and his wife

Sophia. The family moved to Essex and Mary entered service. Later she returned to Norfolk and trained as a

district nurse. To help get about, in the 1920s Mary became the proud owner of a motorbike. In 1931, at the age of 35, Mary married Alan John George Golden and thus became known as Nurse

Golden. Alan was a first cousin of John Golden and of Nolan Golden, a noted bell-ringer. Mary and Alan lived in part of the thatched dwelling just north of the Manor House. When, in summer 1960, she died at the relatively young age of 64, Mary's life and her devotion to her nursing duties were not forgotten, and the table with its plaque was commissioned in her memory. More than 50 years later, the table remains in place against the west wall of Northrepps church.

Frank's son, John, also contributed his handiwork to the church. Churchwarden Janet Payne recalls an occasion when John, hearing that candlesticks were needed for the children's Christmas procession, promptly made twelve hardwood candlesticks. Refusing any payment, John quietly made a gift of them to the church. The candlesticks remain in good condition to this day.

To most people, the celebration of the link between agriculture and church is the harvest thanksgiving service, usually held in September at the end of the harvest season. However, over many centuries an equally significant occasion in the English church calendar was Plough Sunday,

traditionally held between 7th and 13th January, on the first Sunday after Epiphany. The purpose was to bless the land and plough for the forthcoming season. On the following day, Plough Monday, the ploughmen might parade through the village. The men had mixed feelings about this event, for it meant that afterwards they and their team of horses had to return to ploughing even if there was driving rain; and always there was the prospect of bitterly cold days ahead. There is some evidence that the observance of Plough Sunday was especially strong in Eastern England, perhaps linked to its Danelaw legacy.

A former Rector, David Ainsworth, having moved to Northrepps from Wembley in north London, rapidly became an enthusiast for all traditions rural. In 1980 he was filmed 'beating the bounds', famously insisting on following the ancient parish boundary even though that required venturing out to sea in a fishing boat. In somewhat less histrionic fashion, he reintroduced the Plough Sunday Service at Northrepps. This called for a plough – naturally a Gallas – to be

brought into the church, and this was seen as a tangible way of connecting church, agriculture and foundry.

A gathering after the Plough Service, Sunday 12th January 1964. The picture includes Rev David Ainsworth (far left), John Golden (back centre), Jayne Payne (back centre), Penny Kirk (striped scarf), Henry Lloyd (organist, white smock), John Richardson (third from right, back row) and Major Anthony Gurney (far right).

Gifts for Virginia

Let us journey to the USA and to the state of Virginia which sits on the Atlantic coast midway between Maryland to the north and North Carolina to the south. The region boasts buildings dating back to the eighteenth and seventeenth centuries. Not far from the historic area of Colonial Williamsburg is the city of Smithfield where one may find St Luke's Church, built possibly as early as 1632 and thought to be the oldest surviving church of English foundation anywhere in the USA. One of the church's architectural features is its corbic gables which rise from the eaves in steps instead of the steady slope usual in more modern pitched-roof construction.

In the early 1950s the parishioners of St Luke's drew up plans to erect a small museum and parish hall in the same styling as their church with its unusual gables. And so it was, in 1954, that the then secretary of St Luke's, Mrs Elizabeth Jordan, wrote to a magazine in England appealing for information about corbic gables. The article was drawn to the attention of well-known North Norfolk builder, John Golden. This was in every sense right up his street, for the corbic or crow-stepped gables on his own Manor House provided him with the ideal show-and-tell opportunity. Moreover, with its exotic overseas element, here was a story that might be carried by the EDP and add to John's growing celebrity status. He seized the opportunity, and a correspondence ensued with John mailing photographs of his house displaying its corbic gables along with, for good measure, its rare Tudor mullioned windows. (As an interesting extra twist, today we may see – just across the road from the old Manor House – a twenty-first-century building development which incorporates crow-stepped gables as a kind of architectural tribute to its much older neighbour.) Referring to St Luke's plans for a new museum and parish hall, Mrs Jordan wrote to John, 'Perhaps your home could serve as a prototype for those buildings.'

Northrepps Church

Sir,—Your article in today's "E.D.P." about my proposed gifts to St. Luke's, Virginia, states that Northrepps Church was built in 1626. This is incorrect; the oak bell frame was erected about that year, the church being centuries older.—Yours faithfully,
JOHN G. GOLDEN.
Northrepps, April 13.

In his transatlantic epistles, John had mentioned his carpentry background and, one thing leading to another, he soon had an invitation to visit St Luke's. In return, he promised to present the USA church with some of his handiwork.

John's travel plans in early 1955 were interrupted abruptly when his father and mother died, but despite the delay the background story behind John's proposed visit appeared in the *Eastern Daily Press* on 13th April 1955. The journalist doubtless was pleased to have penned an interesting piece. Unfortunately he had made one slip-up, having assumed the bell-tower date of 1626 applied to the entire building. This error did not go unnoticed and, within hours, John fired off a short sharp correction which the paper published the following day.

The gifts that John intended to carry to St Luke's in Virginia were said to be a missal stand, which is a lectern for an altar, and a credence shelf, which is a small side table used in certain church services. Both of these were to be crafted from the same, apparently plentiful, supply of bell-tower oak beams used by his father a few years earlier to create the anniversary table donated to the church. Although these plans were carried in the press report in 1955, it was to be a further two years before John's Stateside visit actually took place.

In mid-October 1957, John's big adventure began. He flew to Washington DC from

In early October 1957 John, with trademark cap, posed outside Northrepps Church with two of the wooden items destined for St Luke's, Smithfield, Virginia.

where he made the short journey to Smithfield, Virginia. He met the ladies of St Luke's, Smithfield and handed over the main gifts and also two carved collection plates. Presumably there followed some discussion at St Luke's on corbic gables

and related architectural matters, and then John was off for a bit of sightseeing in Washington DC, Buffalo on the edge of Lake Erie and the nearby Niagara Falls.

Like any visitor on his first trip to a new country, John sent postcards home; one tourist-typical message, postmarked 26th October 1957, was addressed to Mr & Mrs J. Richardson in Church Street, and reads :

> I am seeing a bit of the US. The weather warm like summer. I am now off to Buffalo & the Niagara Falls. Tell Cyril Proley I have not heard any bell rung only carillion here in Washington.
> Hope everything is going on alright shall seem strange when I get home as the traffic drives on the RH side of the road & bus do about 70 on the open road. JGG

One minor but intriguing aspect of John's visit was his discovery of a hymn tune called Northrepps. Although little commented on at the time, we can surely detect the thoughtful efforts of the kind ladies of St Luke's in allowing John to think that mere chance caused him to stumble across a remarkable coincidence.

In addition to his main pieces, John also presented two carved collection plates.

The Northrepps hymn tune was composed in 1887 by Josiah Booth who also wrote about a hundred other such tunes. He was born in Warwickshire in 1852, became an organist of the Wesleyan Chapel, Banbury and afterwards studied at the Royal Academy of Music. One set of words for the Northrepps hymn was written by Thomas Freckleton. There are five verses, and the second one – with its

Like any visitor on his first trip to a new country, John sent postcards home.

rather stern Victorian language – is :

The toil of brain, or heart, or hand;
Is man's appointed lot
He who Thy call can understand
Will work, and murmur not.

'Work and murmur not' sounds like a suitable motto for John himself.

Church work

During the 1950s John was frequently asked to carry out maintenance on the fabric of the church and this responsibility, coupled with his lengthy tenure as churchwarden, gave him a strong proprietorial interest in the building. An insight into this attitude arose in 1955 when he had occasion to use lead to repair the church tower roof which, he then discovered, had been patched in an inferior manner some 19 years earlier. John thought about this situation for some time – two years, in fact – and then in 1957, no doubt rueing the absence of village stocks (which he always claimed had stood just outside the church gates on the earth patch now used for parking), he determined that the next most effective public admonishment would be a letter to the local newspaper. The reckless guilty men from two decades earlier had to be shamed even if not named.

John undertook construction and repair work on other local churches and buildings. Whilst some might expect such assignments to be subject to careful forward planning, with suitable training

for his staff, this was about as likely as a cow casting a cooking-pot. On more than one occasion a young employee, unfamiliar with the techniques for rebuilding, say, a chimney, would be told to go off and find out for himself by getting on with the job and paying close

Church Roofs

Sir—I hope the people responsible for the upkeep of our Norfolk church roofs will take heed of the warning given by the Rev. A. R. B. Wylam and use materials that have stood the test of time and weather.

In this parish our church tower roof was stripped of the lead which had become badly cracked (having been laid in 1731) in 1936 and asphalt was used under the impression that it would be permanent. This proved to be far from the truth, as although it was coated biennially with bitumen solution and the cracks stopped when necessary, it failed to give protection by 1955, when I replaced it with lead.

But this was not the whole tale, as some of the timber that had remained sound under the lead since 1731 had so decayed it had to be replaced. Had lead been used in 1936 all this expense would have been saved.—Yours faithfully,

JOHN G. GOLDEN.
(Churchwarden).

attention as he dismantled the old one.

After John's death, his widow asked Bill Pardon, a skilled carpenter, to make a

Bill Pardon putting the finishing touches to the table in his workshop at his home in Trimingham.

special table to commemorate John. The table now serves as the temporary altar sited to the left of the pulpit. A brass plaque fixed on the lower cross-bar reads:

In memory of
John George Golden
1905-1989
Church Warden of this Parish
for over 58 years

Towards the end of his long term as churchwarden, John attended a special service in Northrepps church at which the Bishop of Norwich officiated. John Golden remained a churchwarden for a further two years, achieving a record 58 continuous years in that office. Although not formally re-elected in 1985, just before his 80th birthday, John was given the honorary title of Emeritus Church Warden.

The Bishop of Norwich with clergy and churchwardens of Northrepps and Sidestrand to mark John Golden's long service as churchwarden. (l to r) Edward Chadwick (CW, Sidestrand), Wallace Allen (Deputy CW, Northrepps); The Bishop of Norwich, the Rt Rev Maurice Wood; John Golden (CW, Northrepps); and Peter Baker (CW, Northrepps). Northrepps Church Warden Janet Payne was unable to attend on that day.

A churchyard is a reminder of those who have been part of village history. As a concluding thought we may reflect that John and his wife Mary, along with John's parents Pattie and Frank and many other Golden ancestors, are interred in the graveyard of Northrepps Church to which they had contributed so much during their lives.

Cars

One of John Golden's greatest loves was a heavy old lady with a square rear. The 1927 Austin 12/4 Heavy 12 with its solid leather upholstery was a particular favourite amongst the 20 or more cars he owned. While some of his other vehicles were left to stand in various stages of neglect in his yards, this sturdy beauty – registration EX 1938 – was treated with the sort of care usually bestowed on a film star. Not surprising, since she was a film star.

As with most of John's special items, there's a story behind it. On a sunny Sunday in 1936, Mrs Annie Thirtle of Beeston Common set out in her old Essex car with her mother and daughter for a trip to Yarmouth. The journey was pleasant but uneventful until, one mile short of Yarmouth, the car stopped dead. They managed to persuade the vehicle to limp into town, but no one at the garage could repair it. The ladies weren't to be thwarted, and Mrs Thirtle's mother, Mrs Rachael Starling, did a deal with the garage proprietor, handing over £50 and the sick Essex car in exchange for a 1927 Austin 12/4. In an era when car ownership was

relatively uncommon, Mrs Starling was immensely proud of her Austin 12, and enjoyed having her photograph taken with the car. When she died, Mrs Thirtle's nephew inherited the car. Later, in 1962, he sold the Austin 12 to John Golden of Northrepps.

Those with a long memory and an addiction to TV drama may recall Danger UXB, a 1979 ITV series featuring a squad of Royal Engineers. Set in wartime England during and after the blitz, the team of brave

The prized Austin 12/4 on one of its celebrated outings through Cromer, thought to be Carnival 1979. John is driving, Mary is the passenger. The significance of the white tape just visible on the mudguards is explained in the main text.

Sappers defused unexploded bombs and at quieter times had romantic liaisons. There were 13 episodes, the penultimate one being 'The Pier', in which all previously-laid British defensive mines had to be cleared from the south and east coasts in preparation for D-Day; our brave Team was allocated Cromer Pier. And when the ITV Producer wanted an impressive and historically authentic car for some of the scenes, to whom should he turn but John Golden? At a critical point during the search of the pier, one of the mines exploded, injuring the hero, Brian Ash [played by Anthony Andrews]. In the centre of Cromer, his girlfriend Susan Mount [played by Judy Greeson] heard the explosion and, crying 'To the pier, quickly!' jumped into a taxi, the Golden

1978. John Golden and 10 year old Julia Burrows beside the Austin 10/4 (DG 4980) outside the manor house. The special notice is fixed just under the radiator grill.

Austin 12. The producer's desire for authenticity required wartime white visibility-tape to be fixed to the Austin's mudguards, and this tape was left in place for years afterwards, affording John many opportunities to explain his car's starring role whenever passers-by made innocent enquiry about the strange white strips. Although it had appeared at carnivals and rallies throughout East Anglia, this national TV programme surely was the Austin 12's greatest moment. Or perhaps its second greatest, since the car also appeared in another TV show called Eustace and Hilda which won a number of Bafta awards. Some who witnessed these exciting filming events noted that John's pleasure in his vehicle's star status diminished somewhat when he learned that he would not be the driver while the cameras rolled.

Early 1970s. Austin Cambridge TYF 162F languishes in the open on the west side of the Foundry yard. It is thought this car was disposed of some years before the final auction in 1989.

Away from the heady thrill of his vicarious TV drama appearance, John often would take his treasured lady out for a spin. Another vying for his affections was the 1932 Austin 10/4. This had the registration number DG 4980 above which was affixed a plate announcing : 'The Oldest (?) Unrestored Austin Ten Four'. That question mark is intriguing, suggesting an uncharacteristic lack of confidence and presumably intended to mollify any challenger to the title.

A reliable eyewitness states that on one occasion he counted 39 cars scattered throughout John Golden's several outbuildings which included a barn at Church Farm in the Loke near the church. Of the total vehicles counted, roughly half were more or less junk, leaving about 20 apparently in a reasonable state (using 'reasonable' in a broad sense). It seems likely that John had bought and sold even more cars over his lifetime.

Potentially the most valuable car John never owned was the Argyll he didn't buy. Were you to contemplate the many splendid achievements for which nineteenth-century Scotland was famed you might not include its automobile industry in your shortlist. Yet in 1899 The Hozier Engineering Company in Glasgow started to produce a series of cars under the Argyll marque and these vehicles, whose design allegedly was based on the contemporary Renault, enjoyed some success for a number of years. Almost all so-called vintage models were built in the early part of the twentieth century, and so to be offered a car built in the nineteenth century was a rare opportunity indeed. John was made just such an offer, and reportedly mulled it over for a long time;

so long, in fact, that it never happened. Had such a nineteenth-century-built Argyll been included in his collection, without question it would have been the star attraction.

Of the many – easily more than 40 – cars which John had owned in his lifetime, those for which there is definite evidence of their existence in the 1980s are listed below.

Year of Manuf.	Make / Model	Number Plate	Remarks
1927	Austin 12/4 Heavy 12	EX 1938	Bought by JGG 1962 Used in TV programmes
1931	1931 Austin 16		
1932	1932 Austin 7 (two-door)	MV 7031	
1932	1932 Austin 10/4	DG 4980	
1934	1934 Austin 10/4 Litchfield		
1937	Austin Cambridge		Favourite runabout
1936/7	1936/7 Austin Light 12		
1937	Austin 7 (Big)		

Year of Manuf.	Make / Model	Number Plate	Remarks
1941/2	Wartime Austin 10		Restricted lights
1947/9	Austin 16		
	Morris Marina	K Reg.	
1947	Austin 16		Destroyed in fire
1947	Austin 16		Destroyed in fire
1951	Land Rover		
1952/3	Austin A40 saloon		
1952/3	Austin A40 Somerset		
1952/3	Austin A40 Somerset		
1968	Austin Mini 1000		
1970	Morris Minor 1000 estate		
1976	Citroen 2 CV (four door)		

As the above table reveals, John favoured Austin cars, which in the first half of the twentieth century were produced at Longbridge by the company established by Herbert Austin.

A few months after John Golden's death in May 1989, his sole executor, his wife Mary, instructed Aylsham auctioneers G. A. Key to sell all the motor vehicles and related attachments in John's estate. The sale took place on Thursday 3rd August 1989 at Key's Aylsham showrooms, attracting widespread interest in Norfolk and beyond, and bidding was brisk. There is no publicly-available record of the total amount raised at auction, though we can make an educated guess. The most valuable vehicle – John's favoured Austin 12/4 – is known to have sold for £8,500. The auctioneer said that most lots sold for better-than-estimate prices. There were 20 vehicles, or 18 if we discount the two damaged by fire, and we might reasonably assume an average sale price of £5,500. That indicates that the total raised – in round terms – must have been £100,000.

Where are these Austins now? It is known that most were purchased by private collectors rather than by dealers, and so we may believe or at least hope that each is still lovingly cherished as a unique car with a special Golden history.

In the barn alongside the Manor House, the 1932 two-door Austin 7.

The Copeman connection

On 1st January 1927 Parliament passed into law the Adoption Act which required, amongst other things, the setting up of a central register to record the adopted name of the child and the date of adoption. Before then, adoption in England had been an informal matter, often within an extended family. The absence of formal rules before 1927 prompted many responsible adoptive parents to have their wills redrawn to include a declaration of the adoption. This removed any doubt about the arrangement and gave the parties the reassurance that everything had been formalised so far as was then possible.

Around 1890, Pattie's sister with the sunny disposition, Minnie Mary, met Walter George Copeman, a handsome butcher from Field Dalling, a hamlet close to Hindringham, Minnie's home village. They married in 1892 and decided to move to London, settling south of the river in Lambeth. Walter prospered in his trade and eventually came to own two butcher shops, in Tooting and Clapham. Minnie and Walter had a succession of children at roughly two-yearly intervals: five girls and three boys, though one lad died in infancy. The last of the children was Philip who, like the others, inherited his mother's cheerful manner. As both family and business grew, all was well in the Copeman world.

January 1908 was bitterly cold. On the second of the month, concern about the effect of ice on the family home in Wandsworth prompted Walter to clamber on to the roof for a closer inspection. He lost his footing on the frosty surface and fell to the street below. He was rushed to hospital but two days later was pronounced dead. It was a shattering blow to the whole family and particularly to 40-year-old Minnie Mary who became solely responsible not only for seven children between the ages of two and fourteen but also both butchery businesses. Walter left an estate valued at £2,458, a substantial sum at the time, but this was little compensation to Minnie who had lost her beloved husband.

Then, to compound the family's difficulties, the young lad, Philip, contracted 'sleeping sickness', a misleading euphemism for polio.

Minnie Mary Golding and Walter George Copeman

The malady left one leg slightly withered and permanently shorter than the other. The family struggled on, with the older girls obliged to become more self-reliant.

To lose one's life-partner at a young age, to have to deal with serious illness in a child, to be forced to take responsibility for a large family and to operate two businesses all on one's own; that would be more than many could face. It pushed Minnie Mary's endurance to the limit. Clearly unable to come to terms with the situation, she became noticeably weaker. In desperation, the eldest girl, daughter Minnie, decided to write to the one person who could provide comfort and practical help: Aunt Pattie in Northrepps. When the letter was received by Pattie, she was upset but lost no time in travelling to London.

Perhaps the sight of her sister Pattie was what Minnie Mary had hung on for. On Saturday 22nd October 1910 – not yet three years after Walter's death – with tearful Pattie at her bedside, the horrified older children standing round, and four-year-old Philip utterly bewildered, Minnie Mary relinquished her hold on life. The seven children were now without a father and without a mother. What were they to do?

With compassion and common sense, Pattie took charge. First she had herself declared guardian of all seven children. Then she discussed with them what each should do. The older children were promptly found jobs, one with the Post Office and others with local businesses. One child went to live with another relative. The two youngest girls, six-year-old Maude and ten-year-old Dolly, were sent to the Brixton Orphanage for Fatherless Girls where they remained for a number of years. Established in Victorian times, this institution, in the spirit of the age, seems to have been a blend of philanthropy and commerce, and the girls' education was paid for by Pattie: for each girl, £5 a year, a significant sum at that time.

It appeared that the remaining and most pressing predicament concerned four-year-old Philip. But that had been thought about too. During that distressing day when the letter had arrived, kind-hearted Pattie, supported by loyal Frank, had decided what to do if the worst were to occur. With Philip being just a year younger than their own child, Pattie and Frank reasoned that bringing up two boys would be no more difficult than raising one. They would adopt

Philip as their other son, and bring him to live in Northrepps.

Seeing no reason to be ostentatious about the matter, Pattie and Frank made no public announcement, and simply told those who needed to know. They agreed that Philip would retain his original surname of Copeman, but to ensure that none could ever doubt their decision, they had their wills amended to include Philip Arthur George Copeman as their adopted son and to leave him a legacy. Thus, through adoption, John Golden and Philip Copeman became brothers.

In 1914, Philip's sister Dolly left the Brixton Orphanage at age 14 and came to Northrepps to join the Golden family. If we look again at the photograph (page 44) of Frank, Pattie, Dolly, Philip and John, it takes on a new significance. The picture truly is of a family.

The younger sister, Maude, having become something of a favourite with the Orphanage staff, was given the charming nickname Blossom, and remained at Brixton for several more years after Dolly left.

After moving in with the Goldens in the

Dolly in her early twenties.

Manor House, Dolly found employment with Rusts (styled without apostrophe) who owned a number of shops in North Norfolk. She worked in their main hosiers and general department store in Cromer, located on the site of the present-day Budgens supermarket. At the time, Rusts was regarded as the town's pre-eminent shop, with its futuristic method of sending coins and notes between counter and cash office by means of small cups suspended on a system of wires and pulleys.

At the age of 24, Dolly married Cyril Langdale Lowe and in time the couple had two daughters, Bridget and Pamela. Now Mrs Cuthbert, Bridget is a delightful lady who kindly provided useful material for this book.

Philip, like his brother John, attended Paston School. As noted elsewhere, the village girls regarded Philip as more fun than his serious-minded brother and it seems that Philip, despite his physical difficulty, enjoyed life in Northrepps. When he reached maturity, Philip headed to Lowestoft where he became a butcher just as his birth-father had been. Later he moved to Sussex.

On 14th June 1933, in East Hoathly in Sussex, with his parents Pattie and Frank Golden as witnesses, 26-year-old Philip Copeman married a young lady whose diminutive stature (said to be barely five feet) was compensated for by the splendour of her name: Claudine Irene Muriel Elise Bellringer. Philip and Claudine went on to have two daughters, Ann and Gillian. In due course, Ann married Dennis Hooper and Gillian married Colin Welham, and both couples now have children and grandchildren.

Philip Arthur George Copeman

Epilogue

Inspiring respect more than affection, John Golden was an ingenious craftsman, successful businessman and man of property. At the same time, he was a person of contrasts and contradictions: intelligent but not academic; talkative yet never silver-tongued; a conscientious worker who kept an untidy yard; parsimonious yet capable of acts of generosity; pious though sometimes a martinet; unassuming but relishing celebrity status; amiable but not lenient; occasionally irascible and sometimes charming.

As a regular churchgoer and churchwarden, John seemingly followed the parable of the talents and determinedly made the best of his inherited business and other assets. He died a millionaire, yet this status was never openly sought and certainly never flaunted.

With a protective and assertive mother, no wife until he was past 60, and without children, John was able to focus his life on the crafts he had been trained in since childhood. Though some consider he never reached his father's high standard in carpentry, undoubtedly John was accomplished in the breadth and depth of the many skills he practised. Norfolk born and bred, he was most at ease in an English rural setting, yet he relished his memorable visit to the USA.

We may ask ourselves what might have happened had there been a son or daughter to whom John could have passed his business. It is difficult to visualise the Northrepps operation prospering in an era of automation and other modern techniques. The cupola furnace eventually would have fallen foul of health and safety regulations, any new casting method would have faced intense home and overseas competition, wheelwrights and blacksmiths today serve only small niche markets, funerals now are managed on a large professional scale, and collecting vintage cars and old engines would have become unsupportable distractions from the core business. In any event, it didn't happen, and John Golden and his multiplicity of crafts and interests are consigned to industrial history.

And yet there is a palpable sense of something valuable lost. Today automated manufacturing processes produce a faultless consistency in everything from a television set to a fish finger and from a microwave oven to a bottle of coke, and this in turn creates and then satisfies our growing demand for and feeling of entitlement to perfection. It is not wrong to want the best; anyone who remembers the 1950s would not want a television set of that era. But the price of manufactured quality is conformity. And our reaction is either to individualise it or to take it for granted. The new family saloon, identical to thousands of others, must have a particular colour or go-fast stripes or cruise control – anything which will personalise it, make it feel at least a little different, and make it ours. And if we have a ball-point pen or other object we're not concerned to make individual, then we simply take it for granted. It's needed but not valued.

That which we really treasure is original and hand-made: a one-off. A schoolchild's first drawing, an old piece of furniture passed through the generations, a hand-carved figure from an overseas trip or a photograph of a loved one. And when celebrities and other high-worth individuals want to demonstrate their discerning taste and good fortune, they follow the same approach scaled up: an original oil painting by a famous artist, an antique piece of furniture, a cellar of rare wines, a vintage car or an ancient unique home. The paradox is that we demand that our everyday essentials be modern and uniform and work correctly every time, yet we save our deepest respect for the age of craftsmanship: for excellence combined with individuality. Within John's own collections, each item invariably had an unusual and valued provenance.

The continuing and growing popularity of local craft groups and hobbies – not least the British enthusiasm for gardening – speaks of a desire to experience the satisfaction of creating something with our own hands. And even when we can't stir ourselves to action, we enjoy television programmes about blacksmiths, musicians, thatching, cookery, painting or house-building. Bookshops have crowded sections on local history covering old trades, noted fishermen, ancient buildings and traditional crafts.

The story of John Golden's life, his interests and skills, grabs our attention in a way it would not have done had he been more academic and less practical. He personified British engineering flair for inventing, adapting and restoring that,

despite our national propensity to self-deprecation, continues to this day. His craft abilities were applied to natural or basic materials: timber from local plantations; pig iron from ore; sand and clay from the beach. He and his co-workers didn't have computer assistance or use automation but relied on their own experience, effort and acumen, and they were obliged to follow the intrinsic character of the available materials. If someone wants an unusually-shaped coffin it might be created from plastic or other synthetics; but if the requirement is for a simple, dignified wooden casket, its shape and appearance will be restricted to and determined by the essence of the timber used. Golden and his men worked in harmony with nature by respecting the constraints inherent in its natural materials.

There is something in us that is attracted to a way of making things which relies on man more than machine, which celebrates the human skill and endeavour expended on creating a crafted piece, and that cherishes the unique artistic quality of an original hand-made item. That was the world in which John Golden lived and worked: where a cartwheel bore the subtle identity of its maker, where planks were

cut from local trees, where casting a metal object required personal skill not only in the obvious way of creating a pattern to shape a mould, but also in gauging cupola temperature, assessing input quantities of pig-iron and handling dangerously hot molten metal with hands slippery from furnace heat.

It was an existence that called for judgement, experience and a deft touch. It followed the spirit of thousands of years of mankind's efforts to use natural materials to create things useful and beautiful, and above all to stamp them with his personal imprint: the pride in his craftsmanship. It is a human instinct that will endure.

That's a cast-iron certainty.

Glossary

Alloy A substance composed of two or more metals

Anvil A heavy iron block with a smooth face on which metals (usually heated) are hammered into desired shapes.

Beer House In a private house, a room set aside for public sale of beer, ale and cider, as permitted by the Beer House Act 1830.

Bellows An instrument with an air chamber which can be expanded to draw in air and contracted to expel air to provide a draft for a fire.

Blacksmith One who forges objects of iron.

Blast Furnace A large vertical furnace for smelting iron from ore.

Bloom A large lump of iron and slag, of pasty consistency when hot, subjected to hammering to create wrought iron.

Bod Alternative name for bott.

Boring Machine A device with a rotating part used for boring holes in wood.

Bott A conical knob of clay or similar material used to temporarily block the flow of molten metal or slag from a furnace/cupola. May be called bod.

Botting Stick A metal rod with a small facing plate used to insert a bott into a furnace's tap-hole.

Bronze An alloy of copper and tin, with the tin content usually at or below 11%.

Carbon A widely distributed element which forms organic compounds notably with oxygen and hydrogen. Invariably carbon is present to some degree in pig iron, cast iron and steel.

Cartwright A person who makes carts.

Cassiterite Tin dioxide, a common mineral; the principal ore of tin.

Casting Forming an object by pouring hot fluid metal into a mould and allowing it to harden.

Cast Iron A hard alloy of iron, carbon and other elements, formed in a mould.

Chaise House Shelter for a chaise, which is a light one-horse two-person open carriage.

Chamfer An oblique face, usually at a 45° angle, formed at a corner of wood or other material.

Charcoal The carbonaceous material obtained by heating wood in the absence of air.

Chill A surface in a mould capable of absorbing large amounts of heat and used to harden the surface of a casting at a specific point.

Converter A vessel through which an oxidising blast of air is forced, as in making steel by the Bessemer process.

Coke The solid product resulting from the destructive distillation of coal in an oven, consisting principally of carbon: used as a fuel in metallurgy to reduce metallic oxides to metals.

Contraction The tendency of a metal or other substance to reduce in size as it cools.

Cope The upper of two boxes which joined together form a mould flask.

Corbic gable A series of step-like portions that terminate the gable surface of a roof.

Coulter A vertical cutting blade mounted on the front of a plough and designed to open the ground ahead of the horizontal slice of the share.

Crucible A vessel, usually metal, which holds molten metal at high temperatures. In a foundry, may be an alternative name for ladle.

Crust The unwanted deposit which may form on top of molten metal.

Cupola A vertical furnace for melting iron for casting.

Cupolet A small cupola furnace.

Die Casting Forming an object by pouring molten metal into a metallic mould, often under hydraulic pressure.

Drag The lower of two boxes which joined together form a mould flask.

Drill A machine used to create a row in the soil to allow neat seed-sowing (as opposed to wasteful broadcast method).

Ductile Capable of being hammered, moulded or shaped.

Fabrication A metal part created by assembling or welding together a number of smaller standard parts.

Farrier A blacksmith who specialises in making and fitting horse-shoes.

Felloe The circular rim of a wheel into which the ends of the spokes are fitted.

Fire-clay A refractory clay used in making firebricks.

Flail A stick for threshing grain by hand.

Flask A wooden or metal frame, consisting of an upper cope and lower drag, used to contain a sand mould for casting.

Flux A substance used to refine metals by combining with impurities to form a molten mixture that can be readily removed.

Foundry A factory where metals are melted and then poured into a mould to produce a casting.

Foundryman A person who works in a foundry.

Forge The workshop and fireplace where a blacksmith heats and beats metals into a desired shape.

Furnace A structure in which heat is generated to smelt ores or melt pig iron or other metals.

Gallas A plough which has part of its wooden carriage shaped like a gallows. Used mainly in Norfolk and perfected by William Hutson in Northrepps' first foundry.

Gig A light two-wheeled one-horse carriage. **Gig house:** A covered storage area for such carriages.

Gripes A long metal device used for grasping a hot metal item such as a tyre for a wheel.

Haematite Ferrous oxide, a mineral which is a common ore of iron.

Heel The distinctive square end of a blacksmith's anvil.

Horn The distinctive curved end of a blacksmith's anvil.

Hub The central part of a wheel into which the spokes are inserted. Alternatively called the nave or stock.

Hutson Thought to be an alternative name for the Gallus plough, after Thomas Hutson of Northrepps who perfected the design.

Iceni An Iron Age tribe whose territory, in the first century BC, was modern-day Norfolk (plus small portions of adjoining present-day counties).

Invar (trademark) An iron alloy containing 35.5% nickel and having a very low coefficient of expansion.

Iron Ore A metal-bearing mineral or rock.

Jill A two-wheeled manual device on which heavy timber is carried at axle-height to keep centre-of-gravity low.

Jobbing industry A manufacturing operation which produces specific low-volume tailor-made items; in contrast to process industry which uses long production runs to generate high volumes of identical items.

Ladle A vessel, usually metal, which holds molten metal at high temperatures. In a foundry, may be an alternative name for crucible.

Loke A private path or short road. Term used mostly in Norfolk.

Limestone A substance consisting wholly or mainly of calcium carbonate.

Limonite A hydrated ferrous oxide; an important iron ore.

Magnetite A common black iron oxide; an important iron ore.

Mild steel A form of steel relatively easily worked and so used by blacksmiths and as a substitute for wrought iron.

Mould A hollow shape to receive molten metal to make a desired casting. A mould may be created using different processes such as sand, plaster and die-casting.

Nordrups An informal name for Northrepps; supposedly the phonetic spelling echoes the local pronunciation.

Parting [powder] The line on which cope and drag meet. A powder used to help separate cope from drag when the casting is to be removed from the mould flask.

Pattern A model or form, usually of wood or metal, used for creating the shape of the interior of a mould.

Phaeton A light four-wheeled carriage having one or two seats facing forward.

Pig iron Iron tapped from a blast furnace and cast into 'pigs' in preparation for conversion into cast iron, steel or wrought iron. (Basic hot metal is poured out of the smelter into a mould which has a long central channel with several offshoots at right angles to the main duct. The overall shape is said to be like a sow with piglets.)

Plough An agricultural implement used for cutting, lifting, turning over and partly pulverising soil.

Plough Sunday A church service, in January on the first Sunday after Epiphany, to bless land and plough prior to the new season's agricultural work.

Plow Old English spelling of plough; still used in the USA.

Puddling The act of stirring molten iron in a reverberatory furnace to prepare it for conversion to wrought iron.

Pyghtle A little-used term for a small enclosure of land.

Refractories Heat-resistant bricks of various sizes used to line furnaces.

Rickle A loose stack of hay.

Sand, Black Common-usage term for sand after use in mould-making; so called because of the colour created through the addition of other substances, particularly coal dust.

Sand, Green A mixture of red sand, clay and moisture (and often coal dust) which is ready for use as a mould in the casting process. The term refers to the unfried state and not to colour.

Sand, Red The raw sand before addition of other materials to create green sand.

Share The cutting part (often metal) of a plough.

Shuck (Alternatively Black Shuck or Old Shuck) The name of a ghostly black devil-dog said to have roamed the coastal area of North Norfolk.

Siderite Iron carbonate, sometimes called Chalybite; a minor ore of iron.

Slag The cinder or vitrified matter separated during the reduction of a metal from its ore.

Smelting Applying heat to fuse or melt ore in order to separate out the metal contained therein.

Smith A metal worker. Smith is thought to derive from 'smite', to beat or hit.

Smithy The workshop of a blacksmith.

Spoke One of the bars radiating from the hub or nave of a wheel and supporting the rim or felloe.

Sprue An opening through which molten metal is poured into a mould. A stick for making such a sprue hole in the mould sand.

Steamer Informal name given to early twentieth-century fire appliance (prior to the self-propelled engine) which was either horse-drawn or motor-cab-drawn, and had a steam boiler to force water through the fire-hose.

Steel A modified form of iron with a carbon content of between 0.2% and 2.1%.

Strickle A template rotated to generate a mould surface symmetrical about one axis.

Tap hole An opening in a furnace through which liquid metal is drawn.

Tapping rod A long rod with a pointed end used to punch a hole in the clay bot or plug and so allow molten metal to flow out of a furnace's tap hole.

Tensile strength The resistance of a material, such as metal, to longitudinal stress.

Threshing Act of separating grain from a cereal plant by beating with a flail or by the action of a threshing machine.

Tippler A large rake-like device, pulled by a horse, used to gather up mown hay.

Tithe The tenth part of agricultural produce (subsequently an equivalent monetary amount) payable to church authorities or to the landowner.

Torc An Iron Age neck-ring, often made of gold.

Trammel A hand-held circular device which, by being 'wheeled' along the inside of a metal tyre or rim, may be used to measure the rim's length.

Tumbrel A two-wheeled cart used for carrying manure.

Tuyere An opening through which a blast of air enters a cupola furnace.

Tyre In wheelwright work, a circular metal rim created by a blacksmith and designed to fit tightly round a wooden wheel.

Tyre-bender A fixed device with three rollers through which a straight strip of metal may be bent into a circular shape.

Wainwright A wagon maker.

Wheelwright One whose trade is to make or repair wheels and wheeled carriages.

Wrought iron A comparatively pure form of iron, with negligible carbon content, that is readily forged and welded.

Acknowledgements

I wish to thank: Ian Thompson-Bell; Bob Wright; Peter and Margaret Burrows; Mary & Derek Manning; Walter & Janet Hurn; Derek Wayte; the late Major Anthony Gurney; Pam Gurney; John & June Richardson; Vera and the late John Woolven; Eddie Anderson; Leslie Risebrow; Ernest Mills; Ann Dunning; Iona Folliard; Peter Bailey; Chris Branford; Peter & Jill Breeze; John Parker; Sylvia and the late Bill Pardon; Alec Reynolds; Janet Payne; Roger Barnes; Peggy & Ken Watson; Dennis Wise; Lorna Fish; Dick Lattaway and Bridget Cuthbert.

For permission to reproduce or quote from archive material, I thank the management and staff at the Norfolk Heritage Centre of Norfolk County Council Library and Information Service, and at the Norfolk Record Office at the Archive Centre.

I am grateful to Ian Capps, Managing Director, and John Capps, former Director, for the instructive tours of the modern working plant at Thurton Foundries Ltd near Norwich, for their invaluable technical advice and for permission to publish photographs.

I am indebted to Dr Alan Haines, Emeritus Reader in the School of Chemistry at the University of East Anglia, for his expert guidance on the chapter on iron; and to Stephen Pope, Research Assistant at Gressenhall Museum, for the benefit of his invaluable knowledge of the history of the Gallas plough. The verbatim record of the April 1972 interview with John Golden conducted by Bridget Yates, then Assistant Keeper of Social History at the City of Norwich Museums, has been exceptionally useful and I am grateful to her for permission to quote widely from those notes.

I have also been helped immensely by the notes and photographs recorded under the auspices of Norfolk Industrial Archaeology Society [NIAS] by Mary and Derek Manning in 1975 and reviewed in 2001. Graham Smith, former Treasurer of NIAS, generously made available additional NIAS material. I thank all three.

The late Verily Anderson had kindly given me permission to quote from *The Northrepps Grandchildren* and I thank the executors of her estate for reaffirming that permission. I thank Iona Folliard for her kind permission to quote from *More Rains* by her mother, the late Ena Morris. For her kind assistance in obtaining extracts from archive copies of the parish magazine and other matters, I thank Ann Dunning. I thank Jamie Edghill for his kind permission to quote from *Cromer Fire Brigade 1881–2006*.

I am grateful to Sue Travis, former Headteacher of Northrepps Primary School, for her kind permission to quote from minutes of governors' meetings.

Admiration and thanks are due to James Mindham whose talent, allied to assiduous research, has created a persuasively authentic picture of the early nineteenth-century first foundry in Northrepps.

In stating information I have sought – and generally found – corroboration from reliable independent sources. Where I have been obliged to use imaginative interpretation, I trust this is evident from the context. Despite my best endeavours, inaccuracies may have crept in, and I ask for forgiveness for any sins of commission or omission; I would welcome feedback to correct such matters. Although details have been gleaned from others through interviews, articles and notes, the responsibility for descriptions and opinions of people and events is mine alone.

Index